THE LOOK THAT
KILLS

An Anorexic's Addiction to Control

REVISED EDITION WITH BONUS CHAPTER

By Michelle Myers

Edited by Keith Collier
Cover Art by Stephanie Cantrell

"Every once in a while you read a book that reminds you of who you can become through the power of Christ. This book does exactly that. Michelle Myers has bravely given a gift to thousands of young women who are struggling to find freedom from the masks they are hiding behind. In a painfully honest, yet beautifully humble way, she dares all of us to trust Christ to be our everything."

Pete Wilson
Lead Pastor, Cross Point Church (Nashville, TN)
Author, Plan B

"For loved ones, anorexia is a terrifying, frustrating and perplexing disease. Through Michelle Myers' personal account, you recognize how it is often the brightest, most promising and seemingly confident women that slip into the irrational grips of this disease. Unlike other books on the subject that focus on the psychology of eating disorders, or recount the tricks, tips and anorexic behaviors, Michelle is able to convey how a young woman with all the markings of success, could slide easily down the slippery slope of fitness enthusiast to full blown disordered eating that nearly destroyed her relationships.

As with many addictions, the lives of all loved ones are infected by the disease. You feel the conflicted pain and confusion of her loving parents and the shame she felt in her own distance from her faith. The journey to recovery is as unique as the individual. *The Look that Kills* is the story of one woman's faith based recovery. Michelle Myers offers hope and a spiritual approach to those who are looking for unconventional treatment."

Chalene Johnson
Fit Life Expert
Author and Celebrity Fitness Trainer

"In *The Look that Kills*, Michelle Myers shares her story of dealing with an eating disorder, giving the reader an intimate look at her journey to finding purpose, meaning and freedom. Myers' openness about her recovery is written in such a way that anyone who struggles with control, perfectionism, negative internal messages or any form of an addiction will find Truths than lead to their own freedom. *The Look that Kills* is a must read for every woman that has ever looked in the mirror and wished that they were someone different."

Terri Stovall, Ph.D.
Dean, Women's Programs, Southwestern Baptist Theological Seminary
Co-Author, Women Leading Women

THE LOOK THAT KILLS
An Anorexic's Addiction to Control

ISBN 978-0-9964009-4-7

Library of Congress Control Number: 2010909535

CONTENTS

———◆———

Dedicated with love to
Noah Jackson, Cole Austin, and Shea Elise

*When the Lord showed me a glimpse into your sweet little
lives, I got the final push I needed to be the woman God
created me to be. The best part of God saving me from my
own destruction was that saving my life made your lives
possible. Mommy loves you so much!*

FORWARD

———◆———

I WAS 50 YEARS OLD. AFTER 22 YEARS, my family and I moved to a new town. I left my dream job, friends that were close—they were like family— and a home that I truly loved. Still, I needed to build relationships and make connections associated with my husband's new job.

Yet, all of those problems paled in comparison when, wham! My 15-year-old—who loved school, excelled at school, had more friends than most, loved life, encouraged the world, Miss Cheerful, Miss Gracious, and my "spark-plug" —withdrew and became the opposite of herself.

Two things kept me strong. First, I had confidence that even though she felt "trapped" and unable to change her circumstances, Michelle realized something was wrong. Second, and more importantly, I had faith that God would teach us His ways.

I couldn't change or fix some of the problems she was dealing with. As a mom, my heart was breaking, but my plate was full. I was juggling a million things. My energy and my emotions were maxed out.

But this was the child who programmed my cell phone display to read "THE MOM." At one time, I had been her hero. My desire and purpose was to be all I could to help my daughters reach their greatest potential. Feeling like I was failing at fulfilling that purpose was draining my joy.

My strength, my abilities, my time – nothing I possessed –could "fix" what Michelle was dealing with. She was miserable. Her new life was too different from the life that had kept her motivated, challenged, and on-task.

The first behaviors were seclusion and privacy. All she did was stay in constant contact with her old friends. My attempts to help her see the positives or brighter days only made her show hostility and demonstrate rudeness and disrespect. Every conversation we had turned into a confrontation. I felt I had to defend my own right to be a mother.

I tried to go out of my way to show her compassion and patience. Many times, I simply withheld what I wanted to say…or even what I should have said. But the fact remained: Michelle was depressed, and she was reflecting all of the classic symptoms.

Once I saw the depression, I became very scared. As determined and independent as she was, I had great concerns for her taking drastic measures that could bring herself harm and I'll be the first to admit that I walked on eggshells around some of the underlying issues many times.

We encouraged counseling, and she did have some, but she never opened up enough to make a breakthrough. Michelle was smart; she just played the system. She knew the right answers, so she could say anything to get the response she wanted out of the counselor. She didn't want anyone interfering with her thinking or decisions.

When the eating disorder symptoms began, I immediately recognized them. I also knew what had triggered her condition, so I just tried to help her work through her circumstances. I talked to her and listened whenever she would take time for me. I let her friends from our old hometown come to visit basically whenever she asked. I even bought the special foods she requested. I never stopped trying to be sensitive and to be there for her.

Rather than referring to her problem as an eating disorder, I would suggest that she eat more of some foods that she seemed to be avoiding and to eat less of some of the "only foods" she would eat. Soon, every meal became a dreaded time and hassle.

I was interrogated about everything I did in the kitchen. *What did I put in that? Why did I fix it that way? Did I know about this new food?* She would make comments like: *I don't like that. I never did like that. I'll eat later. I'm not hungry. I need to study.*

She requested having her own scale for her bathroom. Every time I saw her eat, she was guzzling bottled water or picking at raw broccoli, cauliflower or celery. She read the nutritional label on everything. Most of the time, though, I simply saw her heading out the door to run for hours.

As her involvement in pageants began, her excuse for her behaviors became the need to get in shape for swimsuit competition. Her overbearing patterns of eating soon caused our whole family to dread meal times. What had once been the highlight of our time together, the time that we had all safeguarded and sensed a time to bond and to share, had become a longed-for memory. Either Michelle was balking about the way something was prepared or we were eating sadly in silence as we watched her pretend to eat.

We struggled not to say more to her as we continued to support her problem by appeasing her with the things she would eat so that at least she would eat. It was such a dilemma. It was a nightmare buying and keeping produce fresh and finding refrigerator space for "her foods." It was also expensive.

Michelle denied herself things she truly wanted and craved by pretending that she didn't want or care for them. I hurt so much for her. Actions she thought showed her discipline only magnified her self-inflicted harm and suffering. No doubt her feelings of "suffering in silence" made her even sadder and caused feelings of anger and resentment to build up. I sensed her having these feelings of us being clueless despite our efforts to talk to her and to reach out to her in every way we knew.

My attempts to show compassion or to help in any way were rejected. My daughter had put up a wall. Deep down, I think she knew I was aware of how bad her problem was, and she resented this. In her mind, since I wanted to change what she was so obsessed with doing, I was the enemy. Knowing the importance of exercising and eating right is important, but the priority Michelle gave these two things went to the extreme. It upset all sense of tranquility in our family. Nothing was normal anymore.

One of the most hurtful things during all of this was that Michelle learned to say whatever she needed to say to get what she wanted. Consequently, it became difficult to believe anything she said. Our beautiful, close, transparent, trusting and loving bond had been compromised to the point of practically dissolving.

She was centered on her having her own way at whatever the cost. My sweet, happy child was gone. We simply relied on God's grace and mercy every day to help keep our sanity and focus. Each day was a challenge. It was out of my control. We had been such a close family and we genuinely cared for one another. But Michelle's problem interrupted all of this.

Her sister, three years older, couldn't believe that we, as parents, were not putting our foot down and allowing her to eat the way she was. She insisted that we should pull Michelle out of everything and have her hospitalized. She knew Michelle needed some "tough love."

But Michelle has admitted that she was so overcome with her sin, tough love would have just proven her point that she was all alone. Years later, she told me, "I knew I couldn't do anything that would make you and dad stop loving me. So while your unconditional love may not have stopped me from my path of destruction, as soon as I was ready for help, it was your unconditional love that pulled me through."

Once she had gone this route for about a year, she knew

what she had put herself through and what she had denied herself. Instead of realizing her problem, she reasoned that to stop now would have made all of her "work" and "sacrifice" a waste. She was headed somewhere. No one or no thing would get in her way.

Her strength, determination, and perseverance that had been such positive characteristics for her when they were properly channeled were now her worst enemies. She was headed for 80 pounds and a pencil-shaped figure. And she would get there, despite what anyone thought about it or thought about her. She was in charge.

The control ended up being the underlying motivation she needed to fuel her discipline. Michelle hated her new situation and where she was in life so much that she was willing to put herself through this pain just so she could be in control of something.

The only time I ever saw Michelle break was during a conversation just between the two of us in her bedroom. I begged for her to let me help her. I pleaded for her to realize that it was her attitude that had to change. Until she decided to see the good in things and to use her influence to help make things better, she would be miserable. I said everything positive I knew to say.

At some point, I said, "Michelle, you have always been so strong. You can do anything." That was her breaking point. Through great sobbing, she said, "That's what's wrong. I'm not strong, and you and Dad both think I am." I held her for what seemed like forever until she stopped crying. It felt so good to have her in my arms. I felt as if she was finally reaching out to me and responding to my love.

I'm so thankful that healing can come. I'm so thankful that we serve a God who is merciful enough to pick us up off the pavement when we pound Him away. I'm so thankful that he restored my daughter to me.

She's learned so much – some about herself, but mostly about the God who saved her…who can save all of us. My sweet, happy child is a grown woman now, but she's back.

Did her problem unravel her life and the lives of those who love her for a long while? Yes. However, Thomas Jefferson said, "When you reach the end of your rope, tie a knot in it and hang on."

Well, through God's grace, we tied many knots, and we did hang on. We are back weaving together the threads of our lives to create the beautiful tapestry God intended for our family.

If your family is in a similar situation, the best advice I have is to cling to God. When you feel inferior to life's struggles, He is sovereign. When you lose hope, He is faithful. When you feel wholly weak, He is infinitely strong.

And while she thought she was starving her body, it was really Jesus that Michelle was craving all along.

May God bless you as you read my daughter's story.

Mary Ruth McNatt

PREFACE

———◆———

EVERYONE HAS SKELETONS IN THEIR CLOSET - SECRET shame from their past they can't bear anyone to discover. I had a skeleton all right, but I didn't keep mine in my closet. I had to look at my skeleton in the mirror every day. It started out as an attempt to become healthier. After watching several older friends pack on the dreaded "freshman fifteen" when they went away to college, I was determined it wouldn't happen to me. There was no way I would start my sophomore year weighing 150 pounds. I decided to make some changes.

Those subtle changes eventually turned into a four-year battle with anorexia and compulsive over-exercise disorder. Over those four years, I lost 51 pounds. Standing 5'4", at my lowest weight, I weighed only 84 lbs. My body fat percentage was lower than most female Olympic athletes. Not only was I eating less than 500 calories a day—sometimes nothing at all—I was also at the gym for a minimum of 5-6 hours a day.

Even after I admitted that I had a problem and needed help, it took me more than a year to return to a normal weight. Though my family made sure I stopped restricting my food, they could not control my thoughts. The fear of being fat haunted me for two years after I returned to a normal weight.

My eating disorder affected every part of my life. I pushed

my family and friends as far away from my life as I could. I checked off my spiritual "to-do" list but refused to have a real relationship with God out of fear that I would eventually feel guilty. I was so close to my "perfect weight." Guilt over my destructive behavior would only get in my way.

As I write this, I am proud to say I am not that girl anymore. I am at a place in my life that is only possible through the grace of God. Not only am I at a healthy weight, but I've discovered a way to make exercise fun. I no longer view my time at the gym as punishment for eating, and I love helping others come to the same realization. Thoughts of food no longer consume me. There's more to life than treadmills and counting calories.

I am married to an amazing man, James, who has loved me and supported me, even when he didn't understand what I was thinking. I didn't think there was a person on this earth who could be more stubborn than me. God knew just what I needed in a husband and he has been a crucial part of my recovery. I thank the Lord every day for the gift He has given me in my husband.

Since coming out of my battle with anorexia, I've been able to help several girls through their struggles with eating disorders. Sure, some were girls I met at church who knew my story, but others were women that God just put in my path. Once, I recognized a girl's pattern at the gym all too well and knew she needed someone to confront her about her problem. Another time, I noticed a girl intensely study-ing the nutritional values at the grocery store. Instinctively, I rattled off the nutrition labels for her without error. I still had them memorized. Right there in the produce department, she started crying, and we went to talk to her mom.

Those situations were not accidental but rather orches-trated by an amazing God who wants to use His children to reach others. Thinking back on the skeleton in my mirror that haunted me daily, I know now that I would never want to go back to that time of my life. However, I would not change a moment of the struggle. God used every internal battle to bring Himself glory, and I feel blessed to be a small part of His story.

As you read my testimony, I pray that God will use my story to speak to you. Maybe this is something you struggle with yourself. Maybe you have a daughter or a wife who needs help, but you're not sure what to do or say. I beg you: give her this book. As someone who has been there, I have crafted my words, asking myself with every page, "During that dark time in my life, would this have spoken to me?"

Many times, my writing sessions turned into weeping sessions as memories crept into my mind all too well. It is my prayer that God's voice will be even louder than the words on the page. I pray for the Holy Spirit to give strength to anyone who picks up this book. The strength needed to confront someone special in your life or simply the strength to utter the words, "I need help."

Even after admitting I had a problem and seeking recovery, I was dangerously close to creating more conflict in my life by attempting to map a plan for myself rather than placing full trust in God. You won't find this book in the self-help section. It isn't a how-to book on eating disorder recovery. In fact, through talking to women who have battled issues ranging from drug abuse to promiscuous lifestyles, the thought life of a person addicted to sin – any sin — is extremely similar. The need to control something and the refusal to relinquish some part of our life to God manifests itself in various types of sin. In my life, it took the form of an eating disorder. It may look differently in your life.

God healed me through His timeless truths, which were written hundreds and hundreds of centuries ago. My eating disorder was really just a symptom of the disease I was fighting in my heart. I was enslaved to sin instead of being controlled by righteousness (Romans 6:20).

This is my opportunity to live out 2 Corinthians 1:3-4. The apostle Paul wrote, "Blessed be the God and Father of our Lord Jesus Christ, the Father of mercies and God of all comfort, who comforts us in all our affliction so that we will be able to comfort those who are in any affliction with the comfort with which we ourselves are comforted by God."

In His Grace,
Michelle Myers

ACKNOWLEDGEMENTS

My Jesus, my merciful Savior: *You are supreme, holy, pure and true perfection. Thank you for taking my flawed and sinful life and turning it into something beautiful for Your glory. I am forever dependent on You.*

James; Mom & Dad; Mark, Melody & Katelyn: *I cannot thank you enough for your patience and your prayers during my years of struggle. You believed I would write this book one day. I appreciate your continual support. No words can justify my gratitude.*

To my editor: Keith Collier; **My prayer warriors:** Candice Armstrong, Meagan Bergeron, Bethany Dowd, Mindy Lawhorne, Elizabeth Parks, Terri Stovall, and Thomas & Joy White; **Special supporters:** Charles Carter, Mark & Pat Cooper, Johnny & Ivette Derouen, Dan & Lisa Duncan, First Baptist Church of Cabot, Danny & Ashley Forshee, Bryan & Deanne Hammons, Mike & Cammye McKee, Kyle & Melinda Oliver, David & Linda Page, Ted & Shirley Powers, Darrell & Sheila Smith, Brent & Jana Trusley, Russ & Debbie Wilkins:

I thank my God in all my remembrance of you, always offering prayer with joy in my every prayer for you all, in view of your participation in the gospel from the first day until now. For I am confident of this very thing, that He who began a good work in you will perfect it until the day of Christ Jesus. (Phil. 1:3-6)

CHAPTER ONE

◆

THE FIRST TIME I THOUGHT I WAS FAT, I was only eight years old. I remember sitting between two of my friends at a school assembly. When I was seated, my legs pressed against the chair, causing the meat of my lower leg to fan out to the sides of my thighs. It wasn't so much the size of my legs that got to me. It was that I noticed that my legs were bigger than both of their legs. Embarrassed, although now I'm sure neither one of them noticed, I sat back on my tailbone in the chair, holding my legs just above the seat, so my legs wouldn't smash out. For the remainder of elementary school, I never let my legs rest on a chair unless they were completely hidden underneath my desk.

I made rules for myself regarding lunch at school. I had to eat less than everyone at the table. One year in particular, I remember this meant eating only a snack pack of mandarin oranges and one piece of whole wheat bread. And of course, once a week, I had to sit there, insisting that I just wasn't hungry. This meant I was famished when I got home from school and I would eat whatever I could get my hands on, only to turn around and eat dinner just a few hours later. Looking back at pictures of myself from third to sixth grade, my weight was never consistent. I fluctuated between thin, just right and a little overweight.

In junior high, something changed. I had an incredible

student pastor, Chris Lovell, who helped me realize what it truly meant to have a personal relationship with Jesus Christ. I accepted Christ as my Savior at the age of six, but I didn't really get it until the summer before I entered 7th grade. I began studying the Bible on my own. I got up an hour before school so I had time to pray for my friends who didn't know Christ. I was a leader on Wednesday nights, Sunday mornings and evenings. I participated in a mid-week accountability group and served whenever and wherever I could. At age 14, I dedicated my life to full-time Christian service. At the time, I didn't know exactly what that meant, but I knew that I wanted to serve God for the rest of my life in whatever capacity He would use me.

Suddenly, it didn't matter that I wasn't the most popular girl in my school, or the prettiest for that matter. I was a Child of the Most High, and that made me feel special. Every day, I would seek to learn something new about my Heavenly Father. Each discovery made me realize how unique and special I was just simply for the fact that my Creator made me just the way I am.

I loved to read and write, so I spent a lot of time just lounging around, but I also played soccer. I don't know how soccer girls are where you live, but where I'm from, we weren't exactly built like the cheerleaders. It would have taken a pretty big guy to lift me or any of my friends on my team off the ground. I wasn't fat at all. I was solid muscle. By my freshman year of high school, I weighed 122 lbs. I wore a size 4 or 6, and I felt good about myself. At 5'2", I knew I wasn't stick thin, but I also took pride in the fact that if someone ran into my leg, it would have felt like running into a brick wall. (Okay, that may be a bit of a stretch, but that was how strong I was in my mind!)

I remained on fire for the Lord until December 24, 1999. That was the day I discovered there was a chance my family would be moving from our home in Memphis, Tennessee to the other side of the state – six hours away - to Knoxville.

I was so angry as I prayed that night before going to sleep. "God, if you take me away from this, I'm really going to doubt that You know what you're doing. Can't You see I'm growing in You? Don't You know that I can't do this anywhere else? Don't take me away from this solid foundation. I know if we move that there's no way You're in this."

The move to Knoxville during the middle of high school hit me harder than anyone, including myself, thought it would. In Memphis, I could walk into Target for fifteen minutes and walk out with three new friends. Knoxville was different.

I moved into a very small community in north Knoxville. My new high school was 75% smaller than the high school I left. Unlike Memphis, this town didn't have any big businesses, so very few people moved in or out of the small town. My previous high school was big enough to where it was normal to regularly meet someone for the first time, even if we had attended the same school for years.

In my new town, everyone not only knew everyone, but they knew everyone's business. It was a new world that I didn't quit seem to feel a part of because I hadn't always lived there. My memories with these people didn't go back to preschool.

I really struggled my first semester. I was so unhappy that there were days that I just didn't have an appetite. I dreaded going to the cafeteria because it meant I was either going to sit down next to someone and feel left out, or I was going to sit by myself and try to fade into the background. I had one genuine friend, Ty Mathews, and we didn't have lunch together. Plus, as great as he was, it wasn't like having the incredible group of girlfriends I had back home in Memphis.

I'll admit it, it wasn't completely everyone else's fault. I missed Memphis, and I let everyone around me know it. I didn't want to get attached to anyone because I was headed back home as soon as I could. I already had a boyfriend. I already had a best friend. I didn't need new ones. I'm sure there were many times I came off like a total snob.

By my second semester of junior year, I finally found a group of friends where I felt like I fit. I broke up with my Memphis boyfriend and actually tried to make the mental move to Knoxville. I had moved physically, but I had yet to move emotionally. Slowly, Knoxville became home. My new best friend had one of those "magic metabolisms." She could eat two candy bars, a bag of Doritos and cheese fries for lunch, only to have every guy in the cafeteria drool over her as she walked to throw her trash away.

I wanted to look just like her. In my mind, it made sense that if I wanted to be her size, I just needed to eat exactly what she did. I did not take into account our different body types and activity levels. By the time I graduated high school, I had put on another ten pounds. But this time, none of it was muscle.

Entering college, I was petrified of gaining the "freshman fifteen." I made a vow to exercise five times a week. I worked in the childcare facility at a health and fitness center, so I didn't have an excuse not to work out. Every night after my shift, I would go upstairs and get on the elliptical machine for at least 30 minutes to punish myself for what I had eaten that day.

You would think that my weight gain would have at least stalled at that point, but it didn't. I lived at home during college to save money. Before leaving home at 7 a.m., I would grab a granola bar out of the pantry for breakfast and head to school. By the time I got out of class at 1 o'clock, my stomach had already been growling since 10:30 a.m. I would drive through the nearest fast food restaurant and eat something that I know now was wildly unhealthy. My minimal exercise could not compete with the food I was eating, so I continued to gain weight.

Halfway through my first semester, my workouts had to stop. I had felt overly tired for a few days, so I went to the doctor. When they weighed me, it showed that I had put on eight pounds in just three months. Forget the freshman fifteen, I was headed for the freshman twenty-five!

My doctor diagnosed me with mononucleosis (and no, while it is known as the "kissing disease," I actually got mine from a water fountain on campus!). I was under doctor's orders that I could not work out for six weeks.

At this news, mono became my enemy. However, we became fast friends a few days into my sickness. In addition to feeling overly tired, another common symptom of mono is a loss of appetite. It took all of the energy I had to go to class. I worked one shift a week just to stay in good standing at my job. By the time I finished my day, I was too tired to eat. When I did eat, I would have a yogurt and some crackers. A few times, I remember eating a bowl of soup.

I didn't realize how much weight I had lost during those six weeks until I went to my follow-up appointment with my doctor. I routinely stepped on the scale for the nurse, and she gasped when she adjusted the weighted tabs. "Girl, when you were here six weeks ago, you weighed 138 pounds. Today, you're only 118!"

My jaw hit the floor. Had I really lost 20 pounds in six weeks? I had barely even walked up a flight of stairs! I don't remember much else from the rest of the doctor's appointment, except for when my doctor told me I could begin to exercise again. In my head, I just remember doing the math. *"If I lost 3.5 pounds a week without working out, how much weight could I lose if I added working out back to my schedule?"*

Walking out of the doctor's office, I remember having a revelation. Working out alone for me just wouldn't cut it. I was going to have to eat less. I vowed that I would do whatever it took to get down to "the perfect weight." I mean, at this rate, I could get down to 105 pounds in a month. I could do anything for a month...

And so began my downward spiral into the frightening world of anorexia...

FOR THOUGHT AND DISCUSSION

◆

1. If you have ever struggled with an addiction, do you remember the first time you ever struggled? Did it seem insignificant at the time, or did you realize you were heading down a dangerous path?

2. Reflect on the time in your life when you felt closest to God. How did the security of your relationship with Him affect the other areas of your life?

3. Just as my faith waivered when I moved in the middle of high school, have you ever been in such a difficult situation that you began to doubt God? How did you work through it, or do you still struggle with believing in Him?

4. In *Plan B*, Pete Wilson writes, "In this life, many of your questions will simply not have answers. But through it all, God himself will never change. This is why our faith must rest on His identity and not necessarily His activity." What do you think that means?

CHAPTER TWO

◆

O N THE WAY HOME FROM THE DOCTOR, I stopped at the grocery store to pick up some magazines. Looking back, I can see it was a sign of the direction I was going. I headed home with six new fitness magazines and not a single thing to eat. I was determined to learn everything I could about fitness and nutrition. I had gained momentum from a 20-pound weight loss and there wasn't a moment to waste.

Now is probably the best time to let you in on a little secret: I'm an extreme perfectionist—a control freak. In my last chapter, what I didn't tell you was that through all of my struggles in transitioning after the move in high school, I also worked ahead in school to take my mind off my problems. I graduated high school a full year early. I had already decided if I could finish high school in three years, I could finish college in three years.

Therefore, when I decided I could get down to 105 pounds, I knew I could make it happen. I just had to decide it my mind it would happen, be dedicated, and do it. I could rely on myself to work hard and stay focused. Will power was mine.

The fitness magazines were just the beginning. I borrowed resources from some of the personal trainers at the gym. I did research online. I explored the library on campus for everything fitness-related. Quickly, I devised a plan that would get me to my goal weight as quickly as possible.

First, working out once a day wasn't enough. I needed to start training like an athlete, and that meant two-a-days. After reading that it was better to work out on an empty stomach, I began getting up at 4:30 a.m. so I could be there when the gym opened at 5 a.m. I would work out for an hour and a half and head home briefly to shower and to eat breakfast.

My morning workouts were intense. After warming up on the elliptical trainer for 30 minutes, I went to a group fitness class. Three days a week I would do an indoor cycling class and the other two days were spent in a strength-training class. I also kept up my exercise routine at night after work, except I extended the time to one hour.

As recommended, I also began keeping a food journal. Even though every page looked practically identical, I still wrote everything down that went into my mouth. There wasn't a stick of sugar-free gum unaccounted for in my diary. I followed a bodybuilder's diet. Everything I read said this was the most effective way to get lean and burn fat.

My breakfast consisted of ½ cup of old fashioned oats cooked with water, mixed with cinnamon and ½ tsp of flaxseed oil. I ate a large apple between breakfast and lunch. For lunch, I had plain tuna wrapped in a whole-wheat tortilla with raw broccoli on the side. I would eat a protein bar before heading to work. During my 15-minute break at work, I would eat 6 oz. of grilled chicken, steamed veggies and ½ cup of brown rice. Following my evening workout, I would eat fat-free yogurt when I got home.

Every day, I knew that 1,600 calories were going into my body, but I was easily burning 2,700. Since 3,500 calories make up a pound, I was creating a 1,100-calorie deficit each day. This meant, I could lose the recommended amount of 2 pounds per week and that's exactly what I did. After six weeks, I was down to 105 pounds.

I couldn't go anywhere without getting compliments. Ladies at church wanted to know my secret. Girls I didn't even know would give me jealous stares when they passed me in public. Most surprising, however, was all of the new found attention I started to receive from guys at college. Growing up as a girl that had always been, "one of the guys," this was new territory for me and I loved it.

I also got the attention of the personal trainers and fitness managers at the gym. "Michelle, you're in such great shape. You look amazing. It's such a waste having you at the front desk and in child care. Why don't you get certified to teach classes?"

It seemed too good to be true. Did I just get offered the opportunity to get paid to work out? It was perfect. Using money out of my savings account, I got certified to teach classes. Within a few months, I was no longer standing behind a desk. I was the one with the microphone in the group fitness classes, torching calories for hours a day. With my new teaching schedule, I was easily burning double the calories I was consuming.

However, something happened next that I didn't know how to handle at first. My weight loss had stopped. I was so confused. How could I be burning so many more calories than I was eating and not lose more weight? I still felt fat when I looked in the mirror, so I knew I still had a few more pounds to go. I would step on the scale religiously every morning just knowing that I would have to start losing again eventually. But nothing changed. My weight seemed permanently fixed at 105 pounds. (Looking back at this now, I can't imagine how I could rationally think in my mind that it was possible for me to weigh just over 100 pounds and be fat, but I did.)

I went back into research mode and came to a conclusion. I remember reading the exact phrase, "If you still need to lose weight and you can't add anymore exercise to your schedule, the solution is simple. You just have to eat less."

Of course. Why didn't I remember that from my 6-week stint with mono? Eating less could easily be done. First, I eliminated my afternoon snack. The brown rice with my dinner was the next to go. I just doubled the serving of steamed vegetables instead. Then, I didn't really see the point of my evening snack. I could just go to bed earlier to forget about my growling stomach.

The second bit of advice I began to follow was to stop stepping on the scale and begin to judge your progress by how your pants fit. The numbers had been discouraging me anyway, so I happily put the scale from my bathroom inside a cabinet and vowed not to get it out again until I wore a size zero.

Eating less worked for a while. My food diary now clocked in at about 800 calories a day. Pretty soon, I was back in the same rut. I still hadn't stepped on a scale, but I knew I wasn't losing weight anymore. I wasn't sure I could eat less. I was already hungry all the time. So, I went back to the books.

This time, I decided I needed more strength training. Of course, I didn't take this to mean that I had to back down on my cardio. I just needed to be sure I was lifting weights to keep my metabolism high throughout the day. To give myself an extra edge, I hired a personal trainer. Since I was already tired most days when I began my workout, I thought having someone there to push me would give me the extra motivation I needed to reach my goal.

By this point, the compliments had begun to turn into concern. "Michelle, you're so thin. Maybe you should take a few days off from the gym. Are you sure you're eating enough?"

Pssshh. They were just jealous that I had the discipline they wished for. The comments only gave me more motivation except now I had a new obstacle to conquer. Everyone thought I had a problem, but I didn't. I just wanted to be healthy. I had to think of a way to help everyone realize that they were the only ones who had an issue with my weight.

I needed a mask and I needed one fast.

Again, a new opportunity fell into my lap. I entered a pageant. The logic was perfect. What person with an eating disorder or an unhealthy body image would purposely parade around on a stage in a swimsuit?

At only 19 years old, I was one of the youngest to enter the pageant. I didn't think I stood a chance at actually winning a preliminary for Miss America but I just wanted the "eating disorder" comments to stop. Besides, most of the girls had been competing in pageants for years, and I was just getting started.

But at the end of the night, something happened that I hadn't bargained for. The crown actually went on my head. The average, good student, little church nerd Michelle was now a beauty queen!

That's when the mixed signals really started. At the same time I heard the concerned comments like, "Michelle, I think you might be a little too skinny," I was now also hearing, "Michelle, you look absolutely amazing on camera."

From there, I went from bad to worse. I now had to compete against 50 of the most beautiful girls in my state. I knew I couldn't beat them in age or experience and they all had a few years of maturity on me in the talent competition. So what did I do? I decided to do everything in my power to rock the swimsuit competition. I just needed to have the will power.

That's when I decided if I couldn't get rid of the weight while I was still eating, I would just stop eating altogether.

FOR THOUGHT AND DISCUSSION

◆

1. Do you think you have the tendency to be a "control freak?" Why or why not? List examples of your behavior to support your answer.

2. How does it feel when you get lots of compliments and attention? Do you think the world sometimes pats us on the back when we do things that displease God? If we know that pleasing God is more important than worldly approval, why do we continue to disobey Him?

3. While battling an eating disorder, I was offered the opportunity to teach classes at the gym and won a beauty pageant. Do you think the world will sometimes offer us "good opportunities" that may not be best for us to take? How can we recognize the difference between an opportunity given to us by God and an opportunity offered to us by the world?

CHAPTER THREE

———◆———

I CUT OUT SNACKS FIRST, THEN MY MEALS got smaller and smaller. Before long, I was skipping entire days of eating. Note, I never dropped any of my workouts. I was now working out with a personal trainer twice a week in addition to my group fitness teaching schedule on top of my morning and evening workouts.

Also, since I discovered that running was a great way to tone your legs and burn calories at the same time, I switched from the elliptical trainer to the treadmill. Still trying to avoid people questioning my new "love" for running, I decided to train for a half-marathon. Then, my crazy running schedule would make sense. I had a cover for everything.

My daily routine was exhausting, yet oddly empowering. I felt I had something inside of me that was better than everyone else. Everyone I knew had to count on food to survive. Not me. I was somehow super-human. I could not only survive without it, but I could thrive. I was in control.

Sure, I would have to break down and eat something every once in a while. Thanks to my continued research, I just made sure it was a negative calorie food – foods that actually burn more calories to digest that you do from eating them. Egg whites, whey protein powder mixed with water, apples, fat-free yogurt, raw broccoli and cauliflower were the only foods allowed to enter my body.

As if that wasn't enough, I began taking multiple appetite suppressants and fat burners. Though the instructions on the labels said to take 30 minutes before meals and not to mix with other medications, I thought I could expedite my results by just eliminating the food part and taking as many diet pills as I could afford. I knew I had to be close to getting to my goal weight. I couldn't give up now.

Because of my school and work schedule, it made it easier to avoid seeing my family. I could manage to be out of the house before anyone woke up and return when they were getting ready to go to sleep. I even made myself busy at church, teaching children's Sunday school and choir and singing in my dad's praise team. As long as it didn't involve talking to people old enough to be able to notice something was wrong with me, I was all about serving God. I thought that if I was busy serving, I could avoid having to study the Bible and feel any sort of conviction that I was doing anything wrong.

My addiction knew no bounds. To make it look like I was eating before I left in the morning, I would either leave the pantry door open or the kitchen light on. Sometimes, I would even pour a little milk into a bowl and leave it in the sink with a spoon to make it look like I had eaten a bowl of cereal. Other times, I would throw wrappers of protein bars in the trash, taking the protein bars with me to toss out of my car window as soon as I got out of my neighborhood. Somewhere in Knoxville, there are some protein-fortified squirrels, I'm sure.

I covered my tracks everywhere I went. Occasionally, I would drive through fast food restaurants since my dad had the password to check my bank statement and instead of eating the food myself, I would give it to someone at work, surprise a friend with lunch or it would just end up in the trash.

I was often home alone in the afternoon for a few hours before I had to go back to work at the gym in the evenings.

On those days I would cook a normal dinner for my family, pretending I had simply made dinner for myself and prepared extra so they wouldn't have to cook. Cooking somehow gave me the feeling that my lifestyle was normal because I was still around food. I just chose not to eat it. Ironically, I actually cooked a lot during that time of my life. I would make cookies to take to work, bake cakes for friend's birthdays, etc. It was all a part of my disguise. In my mind, preparing food to give to others not only would ease people's minds that I didn't have a problem, but it would also ensure that they would never be skinnier than me.

I was always prepared with a great story when I got home from work – where I had eaten dinner, who I had eaten with, how stuffed I was, how I couldn't imagine eating another bite – just in case I was asked a question. I always had an answer ready. Plus, the comments about being too skinny were starting to get really annoying.

To avoid people from noticing how thin I was, I would wear really baggy clothes so you couldn't see where the clothes stopped and I began.

On days when I had to dress up more, I put sweat pants on underneath my jeans to make them fit. Plus, I never went anywhere without a sweatshirt. Not only did it help disguise my figure, but my body fat was so low, I couldn't even keep myself warm in the 90-degree summer heat.

My parents not only began to believe me, they eventually stopped asking me anything food-related. Honestly, my excuses were so good, they couldn't seem to catch me.

"Your mother and I decided to replace all of our prying with praying," my dad told me several years later. "You weren't listening to us, so we just hoped that you would listen to God before it was too late."

By the time the Miss Tennessee pageant rolled around, I was smaller than I had ever been. While shopping for clothes for the pageant I was thrilled to discover that I was no longer a size zero. I had to buy zeros and then have them taken in to fit me.

Backstage, the girls all fussed over how thin I was – how it was unfair to have to walk on stage after me. While I was half-listening to their complaints, I was more preoccupied with how I looked in the mirror. While I was hanging out in the hotel room of one of the other contestants, I couldn't take my gaze off of my trouble spots in her full-length mirror and found myself wishing my tummy would be just a little smaller.

Finally, I clued in to their conversation, "I bet you don't even weigh 90 pounds," one of the other contestants challenged.

"Sure, I do," I said, quickly, "I weigh 105," although the last time I had stepped on a scale was nearly ten months earlier.

"Not buying it. Prove it," she dared, pointing to her scale in the bathroom. I swallowed hard. You would have thought I was walking to the gallows to be hung the way I was dreading stepping on that scale. What if I had gained weight? What if they actually thought I was fat and were just waiting on an opportunity to make fun of me?

Taking a deep breath, I stepped on the scale, closing my eyes.

My heart skipped a beat. I had to physically stop myself from gasping out loud. With victory, she shouted, "Aha! I was right! 89 pounds, everyone!"

I don't remember if I said anything to her. I just know her words kept echoing in my brain. *89 pounds.* I knew the shoes and earrings I was wearing would alone weigh at least three pounds.

I know 89 pounds is skinny, I thought to myself. *Maybe even too skinny. But why do I still feel fat?* I was so confused, but one thing finally became clear to me: I had a problem.

FOR THOUGHT AND DISCUSSION

◆

1. Have you ever had to work really hard to cover up and justify your sin? Why do you think telling multiple lies still isn't enough of a red flag to make us stop and repent?

2. If you've ever battled an addiction, have you ever surprised yourself, like I did when I saw 89 lbs. on that scale, with how deep you've gotten into sin? Describe that moment.

3. When you first realized you had a problem, what did you do? Did you continue to mask it like I did, or did you immediately seek help? Why?

CHAPTER FOUR

———◆———

EVERYONE TELLS YOU ADMITTING YOU HAVE A PROBLEM is the first step. What they don't tell you is what to do when you feel like you've gotten yourself into a mess you don't know how to get out of. I couldn't bear the thought of disappointing my parents. I didn't want to have to go through therapy. I didn't want to have to leave my job or put college on hold. More than that, though, I didn't want to eat. I couldn't bear the thought of gaining weight. I would have rather died than live being fat.

Yet, my battle with food was just the beginning of the problem. Obviously, I knew valuing a skinny corpse over a healthy, living, breathing body could only mean one thing: I was crazy.

There was only one thing left to do. I needed to quit fighting and let food and the mirror win. I would just accept that I was afraid of food and continue to do whatever it took to cover my tracks, as long as I could keep it up. I had trouble sleeping and there were nights I overheard my parents and sister, Melody, come into my room just to check on me.

"I just knew one of those times I went in there, you wouldn't be breathing," Melody told me during my recovery. "It was my biggest fear. You denied you had a problem by never being home and when you were home, you were locked up in your room. Your body looked like a shell because there was no light in your eyes. I seriously thought that I would bury my little sister."

I knew I was hurting all of them. I heard my mom's sniffles and saw the dark circles under my dad's eyes. I felt my sister pulling away from me like she knew she had to let go. It was like I had already died.

Death. That was a thought that both intrigued me and terrified me at the same time. I admit, there were nights I went to bed hoping I wouldn't wake up, just so it could all be over. But there was also a part of me that feared God enough to know I wasn't walking with Him. Sure, I still volunteered regularly at my church, but I had completely abandoned my personal relationship with Christ. I knew the Sunday school answers. I knew the public prayers to pray. But, as far as being real with God? No way. I couldn't force myself to think about how much I was hurting Him.

Sure, He might have wanted to use me back when I was in junior high. I was a spunky kid who would do anything to help others grow in their walk with Him. I didn't really care what other people thought about me because I knew their opinion didn't matter. I had confidence that 1 Corinthians 7:31 was true: this world was passing away and my relationship with God was all I needed to satisfy me.

But, I wasn't that girl anymore. I didn't know where she was. How could God possibly use the girl who held communion in her mouth without swallowing? I would wait until the prayer, sneak out of the aisle to the bathroom and spit the bread and grape juice into the toilet. I couldn't even bring myself to sacrifice 10 calories to remember the fact that He suffered a horrible death and sacrificed himself so I could spend eternity with Him. It was also getting harder to hide my problem at work. My lack of eating and now 7-8 hours of working out each day was really starting to wear on me. On two different occasions, I passed out while I was on the clock, but fortunately it was never for more than a few seconds.

My boss saw it happen one time, and she immediately picked up the phone to call my dad. I gained consciousness just in time to stop her from dialing the last number. Though I tried to pretend like it was no big deal, it really scared me. Looking back, I think this was God's way of attempting to warn me. It didn't work. I continued to ignore Him and the people He used in my life to try to help me.

By this point in time, most of my friends had given up on trying to talk to me. That all changed, however, when I ran into Ty, the first real friend I made after moving to Knoxville.

I remember walking into homeroom on the first day at my new school junior year, not knowing a soul. He smiled at me, which immediately gave me a sense of comfort. He had kind eyes. But it didn't stop there. He said, "Hey, what's your name? Where are you from?"

"Michelle from Memphis," I said quickly, once I realized that he actually was talking to me.

"Well, hi, Michelle from Memphis. I think I'll call you the Memphibian." He began laughing and I quickly joined in. Laughing felt good. After more discussion, I learned that he felt called to ministry and was a leader in his youth group. We became fast friends. In fact, during our first semester, we planned a youth revival together that still happens every year in Knoxville.

The second semester of my senior year, Ty had a serious girlfriend and I was dating someone so we spent less and less time together. By the time I was deep into my eating disorder, I hadn't spoken to Ty in months.

I lived next door to one of Ty's friends, Scott. I came home from work one day and saw his car parked next door. Immediately not wanting him to see me, I tried to rush into the house before he could spot me.

"Michelle from Memphis!" he hollered. Reluctantly, I turned around to discover he was in Scott's backyard. I waved, wondering if that would be it, but he was already walking toward me.

He ran up to me with the same Ty smile that comforted me the first time I met him. As he got closer, I saw his face fall. "Are you okay?" he asked.

I turned my head away, fighting back tears. *Come on, Michelle, fight it,* I coached myself. Out loud I said, "Of course I'm okay. I'm better than okay. I just taught three classes at the gym and ran five miles. Never felt better."

"Oh," he said. "Yeah, I heard that you've been working a lot. How's your life with J.C.?"

"Jesus and I are just as tight as ever," I almost choked on my words they were so false. "I pray when I run." More lies.

"You know, you don't have to work out for Him to love you, right?" He smiled, but I could tell he was still concerned.

"Sure, but my body is His temple, right?" I threw back. "Just want to make sure it's strong and healthy for Him."

"Right," he said. "So anything else going on?"

"Oh, not much," I said. "Just got back from Miss Tennessee. Finished in the Top 15. Same ol', same ol'," I brushed it off as if it was no big deal, but secretly, I really wanted him to be impressed.

"Yeah, I heard about that too," he said. "Never really thought that would be something you were into, but if you're happy, congratulations.".

"Well, I'm happy," I said, "So thanks." I was intentionally short with him because I knew if I was around him for too long, I might not be able to contain my emotions. I was hoping he would get the hint and go back to Scott's.

"Hey, are your parents' home?" he asked, "I haven't seen them in forever." Both of my parent's cars were there. "I'm not sure," I said.

"Let's go check!" Ty turned back toward Scott's house. "I'll be back in a little bit!" Scott nodded, and we walked into the house.

My parents, of course, were thrilled to see me with Ty. It had been a while since I had hung out with any of my friends. When I would sit at home on Friday and Saturday night, they would ask, "Why don't you call one of your friends and go do something fun?" One small problem: Fun and friends usually involved food, and that was not an option. We ended up talking for more than an hour. "Our entire conversation was about your workouts and pageants," Ty recalls. "I could tell you had not been eating and had given your life completely to working out. With a mom as a counselor, I knew the signs of eating disorders and you had every one of them. You had bruises and you were so tiny that it didn't look good. It looked unhealthy."

Finally, Ty admitted that he should probably get back to Scott's house so I walked him to the door. While we were standing in the driveway he said, "Michelle, do you think that maybe you're overdoing it a little bit with the exercise thing? And are you eating enough?"

"Ty," I said, "Really? You're an athlete. That's all I am. My job requires me to be an athlete, so I'm training like one. It's not a big deal."

"You didn't answer my question, Michelle," he said firmly, although I knew his adamancy was grounded in concern. "I know you have a problem. Have you talked to anyone? Would you talk to me, or maybe to my mom?"

"Ty, I don't have a problem." Tears were seconds away from pouring down my face. "It was good to see you."

He hugged me. "I'm not going to let you get away with this, you know," he said, "Call me whenever you decide you're ready to talk."

After he walked away, I put the garage door down and slumped behind my car and cried until I didn't have any tears left. I cried because he didn't believe me. I cried because I couldn't remember the last time I had let anyone hug me. But most of all, I cried because I knew he was right.

That conversation was another wake-up call from God that I chose to ignore and take it from me, God does not like to be ignored. But that didn't last forever. On April 14, 2005, He finally got my full attention.

FOR THOUGHT AND DISCUSSION

◆

1. For those of you who battled an addiction, what was it like to watch those who cared about you? Did you see how you were hurting them? If you have watched someone suffer from an addiction, how did it make you feel?

2. Have you ever felt like you've gotten so far away from God that there's no way He could ever use you again? If so, do you think that is true? What are some verses in Scripture to support your opinion?

3. If you struggled with an addiction, do you feel like you were a completely different person during that time? Did you ever miss the person you were before you were addicted?

4. Did you ever have any "wake-up" calls from God to try and pull you out of your destructive lifestyle? What happened, and how did you respond?

CHAPTER FIVE

———◆———

NOW TRAINING FOR A FULL MARATHON, I TOOK off to a park about 10 minutes from my parent's house to complete my last long run. Twenty miles was on the training plan, and it didn't matter that I hadn't had a meal in 13 days. I was superhuman, right?

Like standard routine, I made sure to cover all of my bases beforehand. I knew my parents would call to find out where I was and beg me to come home, so I purposely left my cell phone in the kitchen so they would have no way to reach me.

I made it to mile 19. My vision began to get blurry as I rounded a corner of the familiar park. This stretch of the trail was completely hidden from the road. Trying to clear my vision, I closed my eyes for a few paces. The next thing I knew, I tripped, and I was on the ground. All 84 pounds of me hit the pavement, and it literally felt like every brittle bone in my body cracked simultaneously.

Frantically, I scanned for help, but I was all alone. I wanted to cry, but I didn't have the energy. I noticed I couldn't see anymore, so I tried to open my eyes. *Oh my gosh.* Reality was setting in. I could feel that my eyes were open, but I couldn't see anything. This wasn't like when I had passed out at the gym. This was different. I wasn't snapping out of it.

I knew I should panic. I tried to coach myself through the fall. *Michelle, GET UP! What is going on? Can you hear me? Why aren't you moving? Why is breathing so hard? Don't you know this is serious? MICHELLE!*

I don't know how long I laid there and tried to move. I just knew I couldn't get up. *Wow*, I thought. *So this is it. It finally happened. I am going to die right here on this track.*

Motionless on the trail, I attempted to gather my final thoughts. I was finally disgusted with myself.

Michelle, how did you let it get this far? I scolded myself. *How could you be so selfish? Mom will never recover. Dad will never forgive himself. Oh, and your sister? Remember your best friend? She's getting married in three months, and her maid of honor is not going to be there.*

In my disoriented state, I still knew that I should talk to God. I used to turn to Him for everything, and now, I didn't even know what to say. My thoughts drifted back to my family. *What will they think when they find you like this? What if they don't find you? What if it's some child headed to the playground?*

Bingo, I thought. *Something I can ask God for.*

Lying there, I prayed for first time in over a year, and I mean, really prayed. Not a prayer out loud at church to make everyone think that I was the perfect Christian – I was the master of those - but I actually went before my Savior with a genuine request.

God, I'm not asking You to live, I prayed. *I don't deserve to live. I know that. But if You could allow me, could I please just get up and walk to my car? That's all I want, Jesus. Just let me walk to my car.*

To this day, I don't know if angels picked me up or if God simply gave me the strength I needed to stand. I wish I could tell you for sure, but what I can honestly say it was through His grace alone that I stood up. I don't remember much about the walk to my car, but I know I made it there. I sat in the driver's seat and reached for the middle console where I usually kept my cell phone. Of course, it wasn't there. It was on the kitchen counter, where I had accidentally left it on purpose. One of my perfect plans had finally backfired.

Well, there goes your last hope, Michelle. The only thing you can do is sit here and wait to die. I drank some water that I had with me, and I felt it slosh around in my empty stomach. I continued to admonish myself.

See, Michelle. You've always heard that before you die, you think about what is really important to you. What did you think about? Your family and your faith. Did you think, "Gosh, I am going to look so fat in my casket? Or what about, I really shouldn't have eaten that apple almost two weeks ago. How about, you should have ran farther! Why did you stop?" NO, YOU DIDN'T!

Suddenly, I wanted to live. Really live. Not count calories or starve myself. *I want to hug my dad and tell my mom I love her,* I realized. *I want to catch Melody's bouquet in June. I'm sorry, precious family. And precious Creator God, I want to talk to you so bad, but I don't know what to say.*

Frustrated, I turned my car on. *Maybe a car running will attract more attention than a parked car, I reasoned.*

I don't remember having my radio on as I was driving to the park but I can guarantee you, even if I did, I certainly didn't have it on the contemporary Christian radio station. Literally and figuratively, I had been running from God for quite some time now. People who run from God don't listen to songs that remind them of their guilt.

That's when I heard it: God's voice, that comforting voice that I hadn't heard in so long. *Michelle, I love you. In fact, I love you so much that right now, when you don't even have the words to say, I'm going to give them to you.*

The radio station began playing a song I had never heard before. Here were the words God gave me as I sat in my car, waiting to die.

On the outside, you think I'm alright.
There's a smile on my face. Everything's okay.
But on the inside, there's a different story.
I've stumbled down this road, and I've got so far to go.
I'm a broken man on my knees again.
Longing for a touch from you,
I need your hand to restore me.
I need your mercy. Take me to the place I used to be.
Use all the pain and the hurt to do a greater work,
And restore me.
I wore my mask, running away from my past.
Hiding all my scars, thinking I'd gone too far.
But He knew my pain, and He loved me just the same.
He promised I'd be free if I fell on my knees and cried,
Restore me. Lord, I need your mercy.
Take me to the place I used to be.
Use all the pain and the hurt to do a greater work,
And restore me.
Restore unto me the joy of my salvation.
So, I'll sing again the song you wrote for me.
Give me a clean heart.
Lord, I want a brand new start like the moment
when I first believed.

By the third time through the chorus, I was crying out to my Savior, trying to sing the words that I just heard for the first time.

"God, restore me. I need your mercy. Take me to the place I used to be. Use all the pain and the hurt to do a greater work, and restore me. Please, Jesus," I pleaded. "Give me another chance. Please, Jesus."

With huge tears in my eyes, I felt God's love surround me. Slowly, I noticed I had regained the strength to sit up. It was like the tears had given me my sight back. Fighting so many emotions, I managed to put my car in reverse, and I drove home. I arrived at my house, fully amazed by God's grace. I flew through the door of my house, immediately saw my mom and hugged her.

Through my tears, I whispered the words my family had prayed for faithfully: "I need help."

She nodded, tears streaming down her face. Within seconds, my dad joined our hug. My parents and I rejoiced because that day, I had finally won a battle. However, the war was far from over.

We sat and nailed down a plan. Earlier that week, my parents had been discussing sending me to a recovery center that had a 99 percent recovery rate. Sending me there would have meant that both of my parents would have to give up the chance to retire, yet they weren't concerned with that. They were willing to sacrifice their right to enjoy the last years of their lives without work to ensure that I would completely pull through.

In that moment, the expense of the facility didn't even register with me. I just begged them not to send me away. I had pushed my family and my friends out of my life for so long, I just wanted to be near them. I needed their support.

They tentatively agreed, but only if they could see improvement. I said, "Whatever it takes, I'll do it. I promise, I'll do it."

That night, I ate a bowl of cereal. I didn't count the calories. I just felt hungry, so I ate. I was completely optimistic about kicking anorexia to the curb. I mean, how hard could eating really be? I had done it before. I could do it again.

When I laid down to go to sleep that night, I couldn't believe all that had happened that day. Entering my room, my eyes fell on my bookshelf where my Bible sat. For the past two years, it had only moved from that spot on Sunday mornings. I vowed to myself then that I would start my day off right from now on. Just as I had done when I had been so close to the Lord, I would start my day spending time in His Word and in prayer.

FOR THOUGHT AND DISCUSSION

1. If you suffered from an addiction, what happened to finally make you realize that you needed to take action against your problem?

2. When I was lying on the track and waiting to die, my thought life changed drastically. If you only had a few moments of life left, write down the first three things you assume you would think about. Now, write the three things in your life that consume most of your time. Are your lists similar or different? Do you think the lists should be the same? Why or why not?

3. Go back and re-read the lyrics of "Restore Me" by Anthony Evans. Are there any phrases or words that really speak to you?

4. Do you really believe that in a moment of brokenness, even if you didn't have the words to speak to God, He would give them to you? After you discuss your initial answer, read Romans 8:26. Does that change your response?

CHAPTER SIX

◆

THE NEXT MORNING, I WOKE UP TO THE sound of my dad whistling downstairs. "Michelle, are you awake?" he called just a few moments later.

"Barely," I hollered back, with a croaky morning voice.

"Come downstairs and eat some breakfast with me before I have to leave for church," he said. Every inch of my body froze at the mention of the word "breakfast."

Eat? I thought. *I can't eat. I ate yesterday!*

I stumbled to the top of the balcony overlooking the living room. My dad stood there with a big grin on his face. "Come on," he said, motioning towards me.

"Well, Dad, I was going to start out this morning by having my Bible study time, you know," I said. "Start my day in the right direction."

"That's great," he said. "And you should do that..." As I began to walk back to my room, he added, "After you eat breakfast, of course."

Realizing that I didn't have a way out of it, I turned around and slowly walked down the stairs. "What'll it be?" he asked. "Some toast with peanut butter? Maybe some eggs?"

Uncontrollably, I burst into tears. "I'm not sure I'm ready for all of that just yet, Daddy," I choked out between sobs.

"You've got to start somewhere," he said. I could see he

was fighting back tears too. Softening his tone, he asked, "What do you think you can eat?"

I shook my head. I genuinely didn't know. I racked my brain for a food I could eat that would make him happy, but more importantly, wouldn't make me fat.

"Maybe we can try some oatmeal," he suggested, smoothing my bed- head-styled hair.

I nodded. Once upon a time, oatmeal had been one of my safe foods. I could do oatmeal. I got up to get the old fashioned oats from the pantry.

"You sit," he said. "I'll fix it."

"No, Daddy," I insisted. "I can do it." I didn't want to take a chance on him adding milk instead of water, brown sugar instead of Splenda, or butter, or anything crazy like that. Plain oatmeal with water was 150 calories. I could burn that off in 15 minutes at the gym without any serious damage being done.

"Michelle, please. I want to," he said, motioning again toward a seat at the kitchen table.

"NO!" I lashed out. "Let me do it myself!" I pushed him out of the way. Before I could even reach for a measuring cup, I realized what I had just done. As I looked at my dad, I could see the hurt in his eyes.

"I'm sorry," I apologized. "I just want to fix it, you know."

I wish I had given him the measuring cup and taken a seat at the table like he requested. But I wasn't willing to take that risk. He was willing to spend over $1,000 a day for however long it would take to get me back to my normal self, and I couldn't even let him fix me a bowl of oatmeal.

He simply nodded and sat down at the kitchen table while I fixed my oatmeal in silence.

As I sat down to the table, I realized beating this thing was going to be a lot harder than I thought. Praying for strength, I lifted my spoon to get the first bite down. That's when the tears started. Instead of realizing I was giving my body the nutrients and minerals it so desperately needed, I just felt like I was undoing my "hard work and discipline." And what did my sweet father do as I sat there and cried while I ate breakfast? He encouraged me. I yelled at him when he was trying to serve me, and he just wanted to lift me up. He kept telling me, "You're doing a great job. I'm so proud of you."

I can't imagine how humiliating that moment had to be as he encouraged his 20-year-old daughter to eat her breakfast like a normal parent would do for an infant. To this day, my parents insist they never felt shame as they watched me recover. They were just thankful for the grace of God.

After about an hour, I finally got all of the oatmeal down. I went upstairs, and my gaze immediately went to my Bible. Though I didn't want the guilt that was sure to come with my reading, I also knew I couldn't do this on my own. I had proven that already.

Glancing at the daily reading plan outlined in my Bible, I turned to the suggested passage of Romans 8:1-17. I could hardly believe my eyes when they fell on the very first verse I read: *"So now there is no condemnation for those who belong to Christ Jesus."*

My tear-stained journal from that day reads, "Simply because I have confessed belief in His Son, God has wiped my life clean. No questions asked, no guilt-trip. He sent His Son to die so that His Spirit could live in me, and now, I can follow Him instead of calories. If I continue on this path, I am only harming myself, but living in Him will fully restore me to the girl that I used to be. Until I am willing to completely let go of my pride and this awful struggle, I will never be able to please my Heavenly Father. But He doesn't ask me to lay it down alone. His Word says I have the power of the Spirit living inside of me, and He can push it aside for me. My obligation is not to have the perfect body. All He asks is for me to be His child and cry out to Him when I need Him.

There is a beautiful word for Father in the original language, "Abba", similar to how we use the word, "Daddy."

God doesn't just want to be my Father, He wants to be my Daddy.

Not only had God given me the perfect word to let me know He had forgiven me, He also gave me the perfect picture of what He desires for His relationship with me to look like through my earthly father. Even when I lash out at God, though He doesn't deserve it, He is there to encourage me as I take even the smallest steps back toward Him, just as my dad had done while I ate my oatmeal that morning.

To this day, the picture of my tear-filled dad giving me praise for eating, just as a father would for his toddler, is the best description I can give of God's amazing grace.

FOR THOUGHT AND DISCUSSION

◆

1. If you have battled an addiction, how difficult has your recovery been? Was it harder or easier than you expected? What were some of your struggles that surprised you?

2. Read Romans 8:1. Do you really believe that there is no condemnation for those who belong to Christ Jesus? Are all of our sins really forgiven?

3. Do you have the kind of relationship with God that enables you to call Him your "Daddy?" Explain your answer.

4. Who are the people you know that have truly been a reflection of God in your life? How have they shown His love/grace/mercy/kindness to you?

5. Imagine my dad crying and encouraging me while I cried eating my oatmeal. Does that description match the God you serve? Do you think He hurts when we hurt? Do you think he rejoices when we take baby steps in His direction? Why or why not?

CHAPTER SEVEN

◆

IN THE BEGINNING, PRETTY MUCH EVERY MEAL WAS a struggle. However, it wasn't the biggest obstacle I had to conquer. In my mind, the titles I had earned like, "my tiny friend" and "the exercise queen" were being stripped away from me. The hardest part of my recovery was finding a new identity. I didn't know who I was anymore.

I wasn't alone in my fears. Regardless of age, women tend to seek identity from their physical appearance. Even as a child and throughout adolescence, my friends and I dreamed of being Miss America, an actress, or a supermodel – anything that would verify our beauty. A 1998 Exeter University study of 37,500 girls between the ages of 12 and 15 showed more than half (57.5%) listed appearance as the biggest concern in their lives.[1] In today's world of broken homes, crime, poverty, and hunger, that shocked me. You would think we would have bigger problems to worry about.

It doesn't end with adolescence. In the United States alone, women spend more money annually on beauty products than our nation spends on education. Over six billion dollars is spent on makeup alone.[2] One thing is for sure, women—God-fearing women included—put too much focus on external beauty.

While it was relatively easy for me to decipher what my problem was, when it started, and how it slowly evolved from cautious eating to a deadly disease, there was one thing I couldn't get my mind around. As a control freak, it drove me crazy that I couldn't get to the underlying cause of my intense fear of gaining weight. Why had this one thought consumed me so much? How had I scared myself to the point of starvation?

Early in my recovery, I went to the self-help section of the public library and checked out every book related to eating disorders. I also bought every book on the topic at a Christian bookstore. I was determined to discover the culprit. Each book, whether secular or religious, pointed to the same source: The media places unrealistic expectations on today's females, resulting in low self-esteem.

It would be easy to blame the media. After all, we airbrush magazine photographs to create "beautiful" icons. The average Miss America is 12% underweight and 2% taller than the average female.[3] America definitely gives out its share of mixed signals. I drove myself crazy trying to convince myself that was the reason for my struggles. I stopped my subscriptions to fitness magazines. I vowed to take some time off from pageants, possibly never even compete again. I tried to think positively about myself. I expected the thoughts that had taken over my mind to diminish, if not disappear. They didn't.

In addition to reading all of my new resources, I was once again spending daily time in the Bible. While I was reading in the Old Testament, I realized that America didn't create the obsession with the perfect body. Society began training the general public that appearance is everything long ago. In 650 B.C. when King Nebuchadnezzar besieged Jerusalem, Daniel 1:4 lists the first two characteristics he desired in those he wished to take back to Babylon as, "youthful" and "good-looking."

I must have read that verse fifty times. Was appearance important back then? "God, is that what this means?" I remember questioning. "Am I reading too much into the text?"

Each time I questioned that in my heart, I would hear 2 Timothy 3:16, a verse I had memorized as a child, echo in my head: "All Scripture is God-breathed and is useful for teaching, rebuking, correcting and training in righteousness." That was when I decided to take the self-help books back to the library. Even my resources that claimed to be "Christian" relied more on secular teachings than biblical foundations. The very problem with these books was revealed in the genre of literature and the root cause: self-help and self-esteem.

The National Association for Self-Esteem defines self-esteem as "the experience of being capable of meeting life's challenges and being worthy of happiness." Pure and simple, self-esteem, as defined by the world, is consumed with pride and grounded in self, which at that time for me, was inconsistent and unstable. The only form of help I needed was the ultimate Helper, God. He would provide the answers to my problems throughout His Word.

In my journal, I wrote, "God, if anyone needs to be taught, rebuked, corrected, and trained in righteousness, it's me. I'm trusting You to change me, and nothing else. Teach me what is beautiful to You, and protect me from the superficial cures from this fallen world."

Rather than looking inside myself to discover who I was, I needed to look at who the Bible said I was. I won't lie to you; I was discouraged at first. If you search Scripture trying to find value and worth within yourself, you will come up empty-handed every time. In Matthew 26:41, Jesus declares "the flesh is weak." He goes on to acknowledge human incapability in John 15:5 when He says, "Apart from Me, you can do nothing." Exposing my human weakness did nothing to help me develop what the world calls self-esteem, but it did help me realize my need for Christ.

Due to these teachings of human shortcomings, Luke writes in Acts 13:46 that the Jews of that day "judged themselves unworthy of eternal life." They were absolutely right, but they were also missing a huge blessing. Though they recognized God's holiness, they also rejected His mercy. Those Jews 2,000 years ago had the same struggle many of us face today. So many times, we refuse to humble ourselves to accept God's grace. The problem is "not an inferiority complex, but a superiority complex."[4] Humanity, as a whole, often has too much pride to let God be God.

I can't describe to you the burden that was lifted when I accepted that I didn't have to attempt to live in my own power. Paul wrote in Galatians 2:20 that "it is no longer I who live, but Christ lives in me." I didn't have to seek out my own identity because Christ had established Himself in me. 2 Corinthians 5:17 says, "Therefore if anyone is in Christ, he is a new creature; the old things passed away; behold, new things have come."

The worldly advice I was reading told me I had to find myself. However, God's Word helped me realize that I would only find myself as I found Him. I had a long way to go, but I was finally leaning on the right resource.

The Bible offered me comfort that the world couldn't. The self-help books that required me to act on my own strength left me feeling alone and discouraged, while the Bible simply confirmed in my heart how much God loves me. He knows everything about me, down to how many hairs are on my head (Matthew 10:30). He even knows how many are highlighted!

Each time I found a verse that would combat a lie from the world, I would write it in my own words in a separate place in my journal.

Here is a compilation of a few of my favorite verses I have gathered over the past few years:

I made her...she is different. She's unique. With love, I formed her in her mother's womb. I fashioned her with great joy. I remember with great pleasure the day I created her. *(Psalm 139:13-16)*

I wanted her to search out her heart. I wanted her to learn that it is ME in her that makes her beautiful...And it is ME in her that others find precious. *(1 Peter 3:3-5)*

I made her in such a way that she would need Me. I make her a little more lonesome at times than she would like to be...Only because I need for her to learn and depend on Me....I know her heart, and I know if I had not made her like this, She would go on her own chosen way and forget me...Her Creator. *(Psalm 62:5-8)*

I love giving her things in her life that she enjoys, and I protect her, even when she doesn't know I'm there, simply because I love her. *(Psalm 84:11)*

Because I love her, I have seen her broken heart. The tears she thought she cried alone, I was there crying with her. My heart was breaking too. *(Psalm 56:8)*

Many times, she thought she stumbled and fell alone. I was there, but she would not hold My Hand. She learns so many lessons the hard way because so often, she refuses to listen to My voice. *(Isaiah 53:6)*

So many times, I sit back. And sadly, I watch her go her merry way alone, only to have her, sad and broken, return to My open arms. *(Isaiah 62:2)*

I am constantly reshaping her and molding her, to renew her to the plans I have for her. It hasn't always been the easiest path. *(Jeremiah 29:11)*

But I still want her conformed to My image...I have set high goals for her because I love her. *(2 Corinthians 2:14)*

I have gotten rid of everything she used to be and made her completely new. *(2 Corinthians 5:17)*

She thinks she knows what I have in store for her, but my purpose is greater than she could ever imagine. *(Proverbs 19:21)*

I am the Lord of lords and the King of kings. Her beauty takes my breath away when she honors me with her life. *(Psalm 45:11)*

She has to wait on My timing, but with Me by her side, she will soar above all of life's storms. *(Isaiah 40:31)*

She is mine. I bought her for a price much higher than she ever deserved. And I did it gladly... Because I love her. *(Romans 5:8)*

These verses were not new information. They were truths that I had known my entire life. However, because I was not living under God's authority, they were just words. It didn't transfer into action. I could not experience the victory God has over Satan. In his book on spiritual warfare, Kingdom Authority, Adrian Rogers says it best, "If we are wise, we will place ourselves under [God's] authority so we can be over Satan's power and deceptive schemes. We cannot have His authority until we submit to His lordship."

Satan has influenced the world so much that some days, it appears like something is waiting to trip us everywhere we turn. Yet, a 2009 Barna Research Group survey suggests that 60% of Christians surveyed claimed they didn't believe a devil exists.[5]

That's frightening. Satan is real. VERY real. And it's when we let our guard down against him that he can have the most influence over our lives.

It's how I got sucked into a life of destruction. I am not

blaming Satan for my mistakes, but I really started getting into trouble when I began being more influenced by what the world was saying than God's Word.

For example:

Satan says, "If you don't look like you stepped off a magazine cover, you are worthless."

But Scripture says, *"Charm is deceitful, and beauty is vain, but a woman who fears the LORD is to be praised." (Proverbs 31:30)*

Satan says, "When you go through difficult times, God has forgotten about you."

But Scripture says, *"And we know that for those who love God all things work together for good, for those who are called according to his purpose." (Romans 8:28)*

Satan says, "God will never forgive you for everything you've done."

But Scripture says, *"As far as the east is from the west, so far does he remove our transgressions from us. As a father shows compassion to his children, so the LORD shows compassion to those who fear him." (Psalm 103:12-13)*

Satan says, "It's all about you."

But Scripture says, *"But far be it from me to boast except in the cross of our Lord Jesus Christ, by which the world has been crucified to me, and I to the world." (Galatians 6:14)*

Here's the bottom line: *Satan tries to put lies in our heads that attempt to fill a void that only God can complete.* He will never tell you the full truth. The Bible calls him "the deceiver of the whole world."[6] He will manipulate the truth to cause you to stumble.

There are two passages in Scripture where we can see Satan's attempt to cause a believer stumble: the temptation of Eve in the Garden of Eden in Genesis 3 and the temptation of Jesus in Matthew 4. (You may want to take a few moments to refresh your memory of these two accounts before reading on.)

When Satan tempted Eve in the garden, he told her, *"For God knows that when you eat of it your eyes will be opened, and you will be like God, knowing good and evil."*[7] How glamorous does that sound? Eve probably didn't hear a word the serpent said after he uttered the words, "You will be like God." Satan has a way of sugar coating our disobedience so it doesn't sound as bad as it actually is.

Pay special attention to Eve's response. She says, "But God said, *'You shall not eat of the fruit of the tree that is in the midst of the garden, neither shall you touch it, lest you die.'*"[8] But Genesis 2:16-17 says, "And the LORD God commanded the man, saying, "You may surely eat of every tree of the garden, but of the tree of the knowledge of good and evil you shall not eat, for in the day that you eat of it you shall surely die."

Do you see what Eve did? Why do you think she added that God said they couldn't even touch it, or they would die?

Unfortunately, I think I know, because I'm afraid I've done the same thing so many times in my life. I am so prideful and can't stand to be wrong, so much that I am willing to make it sound like it is God's fault. I picture Eve grumbling, "That mean old God won't even let us touch it, and it's right in the middle of the garden! I have to walk past it dozens of times every day. He could have at least put it in the corner where I don't see it." The more she talks, the more indignant she gets. Before she realizes what's happened, she's taken a bite of the fruit, and her life is changed forever.

Before we come down too hard on Eve, though, we do the same things:

"God is so mean. He created sex, but He won't even let us have it!" Yes, He will. He just wants us to have sex His way, within the boundaries of marriage.

"Why am I the one that has to be submissive to my husband? Why can't he submit to me? God obviously thinks

I'm weak." Jesus submitted to the Father. Just as we don't consider Him to be any less God than the Father, women are no less important to God because they submit to their husbands.

"Why did God create her to be prettier than me? She just shows up to church whenever she feels like it and occupies a pew. I serve in almost every ministry we've got!" God looks at our hearts, not our appearance. It's our fear of the Lord that makes us beautiful because everything else passes away (1 Samuel 16:7, Proverbs 31:30).

Here's where Satan gets tricky. He tells a half-truth here instead of a blatant lie. In Genesis 3:22, God says, *"Behold, the man has become like one of us in knowing good and evil."* However, Satan left out the fact that disobeying God, or sin, results in separation from God. Satan will never tell you the full truth. It is not in his nature. Just as we need to know God well enough to be able to discern His voice[9], we also need to be able to identify Satan's lies.

This is where we can really notice the difference between Eve's temptation account in Genesis and what Jesus does as recorded in the New Testament. Eve gives in. She eats of the fruit and gives some to her husband. Punishment follows that has affected all humankind. No matter how appealing the temptation may be, our goal must be to obey God to the fullest, just as Jesus did. Our Savior is the perfect of example of what we should do when Satan tempts us.

As we study Jesus' response to temptation, we see one thing clearly: Satan's tricks worked on Eve. He is sometimes successful with the very same tactics on us today but his manipulation was no match for the majesty of our Lord Jesus Christ.

I remember the first time I read the account of the temptation of Jesus. *That's it?* I thought. *No angels sweeping down to pick Satan up by his ears and drop him over a cliff? No lightening bolt from Jesus' finger aimed right at the devil?* I didn't realize the power behind this passage. Jesus didn't use divinity to defend Himself against Satan. If He had defended Himself using divinity, how would we be able to follow His example? After all, we are not God. Jesus chose to use the sword of Scripture because God has given us the same weapon. Jesus used the devil's temptation as a way to teach us how to protect ourselves from the enemy.

I love Jesus' response in Matthew 4:4. He doesn't lash out or show fear. He doesn't overreact, but He also doesn't ignore Him. He simply informs Satan that He is more concerned with obeying God's Word than meeting His physical need for food. Jesus knows that He's hungry, but He also knows that feeling is temporary. The consequences of disobeying God are far worse than feeling hungry for a little while longer. He's already gone 40 days without food. God has sustained Him this long, why would He have reason to doubt that God would provide?

Satan didn't give up after one try with Jesus. In fact, the devil is smug enough to try to play games with Jesus. In verse 6, Satan quotes Psalm 91:11-12. Let that sink in for a moment. Satan quoted Scripture. (Side note: If Satan knows God's Word, how much more important is it for God's children to know His Word? Hello, conviction!)

During the devil's second temptation, he attempts to attack Jesus' pride and God's protection. I don't have to tell you that from the elementary school playground to the high school locker room and office breakroom, guys are always challenging each other. Who has the most "man points?" Who can bench press the most weight? Who can eat the most food in the shortest time? Men are always trying to prove how tough they are. Satan challenges Jesus to throw himself off the summit of the temple. After all, Scripture says the angels will save Him.

Picture it. *Jesus rolls His eyes in frustration at Satan. "Fine!" He says. Without hesitation, Jesus takes a running leap off the pinnacle. Immediately, a swarm of angels sweep down from heaven, catch Jesus, and on their ascension*

back to heaven, they gently place Jesus at the exact point
where he just jumped. Jesus folds his arms across His chest.
"Anything else, Satan, or are we done here?"

As fun as it sounds, thankfully, Jesus didn't do that. He
simply responds with instruction from His Father – which is
the same written Word that God has given us.

Satan's third and final try is actually quite comical. After
they arrive on a mountaintop, Satan insists that He will give
Jesus all of the kingdoms of this world if He bows to worship
him. Yet, Psalm 2:7-8 says, *"I will tell of the decree: The*
LORD said to me, 'You are my Son; today I have begotten
you. Ask of me, and I will make the nations your heritage,
and the ends of the earth your possession." Jesus already has
what Satan tries to offer Him!

When Satan tempts Jesus to be like God, when He
already is God, Jesus has had enough. *"Then Jesus said to*
him, "Be gone, Satan! For it is written, 'You shall worship
the Lord your God and him only shall you serve.'"[10] After
telling Satan to flee, once again, Jesus quotes Scripture, from
Deuteronomy 6:4. Not only does he use the same sword God
has given us, but he also pierces the sword into the heart of
the real issue at stake. We were created to worship and serve
God only.

When Jesus spoke about the devil, He said, "He was a
murderer from the beginning, and has nothing to do with
the truth, because there is no truth in him. When he lies, he
speaks out of his own character, for he is a liar and the father
of lies."[11] Rest in this truth: Satan can't give you anything
better than God's plan for you. 2 Peter 1:3 says, "His divine
power has granted to us all things that pertain to life and
godliness, through the knowledge of him who called us to
his own glory and excellence."

If anyone could have created a loophole to justify being
worshipped on earth, Jesus could have. He knew the price
He was going to pay on the cross. He knew the free gift that
would be available to all because of His obedience. But He

didn't try to take any of the glory. He didn't try to make any excuses or validate His reasoning. He simply put the focus back on God the Father.

I am ashamed to admit that I have spent more of my life trying to figure out exactly where the boundaries of sin were so I could go as far as I possibly could than I have spent trying to be as holy as God has called me to be. That hurts to share, but it is so true. The saddest part is that this ultimately means that I have spent more of my life trying to get closer to Satan than I have spent clinging to God and His holiness. Let that sink in for a minute. Why would we ever want to choose death over life? Why would we choose lies over truth? Who could possibly desire evil over good?

But by our own power in our corrupt human nature, we do just that every single time we fall into sin. Maybe you know how it feels to be trapped in sin. If you don't, I can tell you.

Darkness surrounds you. It gets harder and harder to see a glimmer of light. You feel so alone. You don't know how to get out, so you keep digging deeper into sin, but never find fulfillment.

On the other hand, look at what is granted with obedience. After Satan leaves on Jesus' command, the Bible says *"angels came and were ministering to Him."*[12]

I don't know what that looked like for Jesus. Maybe they physically came, talked to Jesus and encouraged Him. Maybe Jesus just went back to praying to His Father, and angels bowed to pray beside him, stroking his back comfortingly. I can't promise that will happen for us each time we are tempted. However, I do know that His Word promises that if we truly seek the Lord, He will draw near to us.[13]

It gets even better! With our Bible as our sword at our side, God never asks us to go into battle alone. He is with us every step of the way, supplying every word we should say.

If you've read Revelation, you know the end of the story. Satan is defeated, and he is unable to keep his false promises. Revelation 18:10 proclaims, *"And the devil who deceived them was thrown into the lake of fire and brimstone, where the beast and the false prophet are also; and they will be tormented day and night forever and ever."* We are not fighting against Satan for victory. God already took care of that. With the sword of the spirit, we fight from Victory Himself!

FOR THOUGHT AND DISCUSSION

◆

1. Do you think "self-help" books as being counterproductive in your Christian walk? Does the Bible offer you advice that the world can't?

2. Do you sometimes have too much pride to just let God be God? As David Myers wrote, what do you think it means to not have an "inferiority complex, but a superiority complex?"

3. What are your three favorite verses in Scripture? Take a few moments to personalize them like the examples in this chapter and share them with one another.

4. According to Barna's survey, 60% of Christians claimed they didn't believe a devil exists. Did this statistic surprise you? What do you think?

5. Go back and re-read the temptation accounts of Eve (Genesis 3) and Jesus (Matthew 4). What are the key differences that stand out to you?

6. Have you ever thought about using Scripture to combat Satan's lies? What are some verses that address the issues you struggle with? Write them

down on an index card, and start carrying them with you. Read them over and over again until you have them memorized. That way, you will be prepared the next time Satan tempts you.

CHAPTER EIGHT

DIGGING DEEPER INTO GOD'S WORD THROUGHOUT MY RE-COVERY, I fell back in love with Jesus. While changes in my physical strength were slow and challenging, I felt spiritually stronger every day. That tug on my heart to full-time ministry that I had felt so many years before was slowly creeping back into my mind.

The months following my fall were like a whirlwind. I graduated college in May, stood beside my sister at her wedding in June, started my first full-time job as a pharmaceutical sales representative in July and bought my very own two-bedroom condo in August.

I loved my new place and my job, but I knew it wasn't what I was supposed to be doing. I had committed my life to Christ back in the seventh grade and that commitment was pressing on my chest.

How was I supposed to fix this? If I quit my job, I couldn't pay for my condo. My parents had done so much for me already. I couldn't put that burden on them. But I also couldn't put my condo on the market without raising a major red flag to my boss.

In November, my boss called me while I was out making sales calls.

Luckily, I was driving, so I was able to answer. "Hey David," I said. "How are you?"

"Hey there, yourself. You know, at the rate you're selling, you're going to end up in the running for rookie of the year."

I laughed. "It's a little early for that kind of talk, don't you think?", "Maybe so. Hey, Michelle, are you in Knoxville today?"

"Yes, I actually am. I try to stay closer to home on Fridays. Why?"

He paused. "How close are you to your dad's office at church?", he finally asked.

I got a pit in my stomach. "About ten minutes. Why? Is he okay?", "Oh, it's nothing like that. Just…why don't you pull over a few minutes so we can talk?"

I pulled on to the shoulder of the interstate.

"Michelle, I'm not sure how to begin. We have done this a few times in the past, but none of us saw this one coming. We are undergoing a corporate-wide reshuffle."

"What does that mean?" I asked, even though I knew the answer. "Well, it means that you still have a job with our company, however, it just means that your territory will no longer be in Knoxville."

"Where would my territory be?" I asked, not believing the words I was hearing.

"That's really up to you," he said. "There will be openings all over the country that you will be eligible for. All you have to do is interview with the district manager, and if you are a good match for the position, our company will simply pay to transfer you to that location."

I didn't say a word for a few moments. Finally, I said, "Do I have any other options? You know it's still kind of soon for me to move…with my whole…umm…situation."

"I thought you might be uncomfortable leaving your family so soon into your recovery. There is one other option, but I really hope that you don't choose it."

"What is it?"

"Well, we can offer you a severance package of two months' pay that will begin after you use your remaining vacation days and benefits. Your job is secure through the end of December, but your package would begin in January.

I couldn't believe my ears. When I couldn't find a way out, had God really handed me an opportunity?

"Look, Michelle, I know this is a lot to take in, and I don't want your answer right now. Why don't you drive to see your dad and take the rest of the day off? We can talk later when you feel like you've made a decision." I honored his request, but I knew what I had to do. I drove to the church to talk with my dad. After filling him in on the Spirit's leading to serve in ministry, I went to see our youth pastor.

When I walked into his office, he said, "Michelle! I've got something for you to pray about." "Alright, sure," I responded.

"Look, I know you are super busy with your new job and all of your other ministry commitments," he said, "but I really want to pray about adding a female to the youth ministry staff to really minister to the girls. You know I love all of our students, but at the end of the day, I'm not a girl. I can't answer all of their problems. Will you do that? Will you pray for God to bring the right person to our ministry?"

Dumbfounded, I nodded. Only the one true God of the universe could orchestrate one afternoon with every detail fulfilling the desires He had placed in my heart. Controlling my own life resulted in chaos and confusion. It was only when I began to release some of that control over to God that my life and my struggles began to make sense.

I remembered hearing a pastor say, "You can only live life forwards, but you can really only understand it backwards." As I began seeking to grow spiritually, I had started praying for God to reveal to me why I had gone through those awful years of self-destructive behavior.

That was the first day I felt like God was beginning to answer some of my questions. If I was called to ministry, especially to minister to women, wouldn't it make sense for me to have a deep understanding of one of the main issues women struggle with?

Going beyond even the practical implications, I felt personally that God was protecting me from some of the consequences of my eating disorder. During that time, I pushed all close relationships out of my life, which included any romantic interest. I genuinely lost my desire to ever be a wife or a mother.

With the physical damage I had done to my body, I had been informed that getting pregnant would be difficult for me, if not impossible. For a woman, I imagine there are few pains that hurt as deeply as desiring a family and not being able to have children. I prayed that if the call God had on my life involved singleness that He would continue to suppress my desire for marriage and motherhood.

He did just that for the next two and a half years. My healing process during that time was extremely difficult. Gaining weight was still hard for me to accept, even though I knew it was best. I felt so guilty for the opportunities I had missed to share Christ while I was in college. When I really paused to reflect on my actions, I couldn't believe the anguish I put my family and friends through.

Yet, I remained thankful that with the chance that the damage I had done to my body was irreversible, God had a ministry for me that didn't involve a family of my own. I didn't even let myself pause to think about what it would be like to look in the eyes of a man that I loved and respected enough to call my husband and tell him that there was a good chance that if he chose to marry me, he was running the risk of not being able to parent naturally.

While I know now that God wasn't calling me to a lifetime of singleness, I do think He was protecting me during my initial recovery time from having to bear the entire burden of my sins at one time. He set the perfect pace for my life's path...which He could only do when I gave Him control.

I used to like the bumper sticker that reads, "God is My Co-Pilot." It's still catchy, but I know my personal struggles.

If I'm the co-pilot of my life, I have easy access to grab the controls from God. Contrary to an actual plane, my life runs smoother when I take a seat in coach.

FOR THOUGHT AND DISCUSSION

————◆————

1. Have you ever noticed that when you try to make all of life's decisions on your own, chaos and confusion follow? Yet, when God starts to take control of your life, things start to make sense. Share some examples from your life.

2. Do you think God normally reveals His complete plan for your life at once, or does He usually provide one step at a time? Give reasons to support your answer.

3. Is God your co-pilot, is He your pilot, or is He not even in the plane? What is the difference?

CHAPTER NINE

———◆———

IN JANUARY, I ENROLLED IN GRADUATE SCHOOL AT the University of Tennessee, went back to my previous job as a personal trainer, took the volunteer internship position in the student ministry at my church, put my condo on the market, competed for the title of Miss Knoxville, and won. Now, it was back to Miss Tennessee. A pageant doesn't sound like the perfect place for a recovering anorexic to go. However, just as the pageant served as my mask for my eating disorder the first time around, I felt like I needed to go back again, physically healthy and spiritually healthy. I had not honored the Lord with my presence at the pageant the first time I competed. Of course, I said I was a Christian, but my life didn't reflect it.

In February at a Disciple Now weekend with our youth group the speaker talked about Jacob wrestling with God (Genesis 32). I knew it was time to take a public step of obedience and I walked down the aisle to my father.

"Daddy, I'm supposed to go to seminary, and I'm supposed to go to Southwestern Seminary."

He smiled at me with proud eyes. "I've known you were supposed to go to seminary for a while now, but we can talk about the Southwestern part later. Do you even know where that is?"

I shook my head. Honestly, I had no idea that attending that specific seminary would take me almost 1,000 miles away from my family to Fort Worth, Texas. Nevertheless, we scheduled a campus visit during my spring break and immediately felt at home on the campus. I decided that was where the Lord wanted me to pursue my seminary degree.

The pageant didn't add too many complications in my mind. If I won Miss Tennessee, I would defer a year and enter seminary in 2007. If I didn't win, I would move to Texas just three weeks after the pageant.

The pageant came, and the crown went to another contestant. Instead of taking that as my answer, though, losing the pageant created a new question in my mind. Was it time to move and begin the next chapter of my life, or was it time to hold off on the move and take online classes for a year before I took the plunge?

I casually brought up the idea of web-based education with my dad, thinking he would immediately jump on board. This way, he wouldn't have to watch his little girl move 16 hours away from home. Not to mention, I was only a little over a year into my recovery. I still had a long way to go.

Instead, he took a deep breath. "Michelle, how important is picking your running shoes to you?"

"What?" I asked. My dad never mentioned running, unless he was telling me that I needed to give my body a break. I seek my dad out as an incredible resource in most areas of my life with two exceptions: running and fashion.

He just doesn't get them. He doesn't understand how it is humanly possible to enjoy pounding pavement until my feet are numb, waking up at 5 a.m. to train, or sprinting with a 15 grade incline at the gym just to see how long I can take it. He doesn't know that a marathon is not 26 miles. (You run one, and then tell me that 0.2 miles doesn't make a difference!) Fashion has him equally baffled. He calls my sister's Louis Vuitton bag "the alphabet purse." He thinks COACH sells sports merchandise and that Guess changes what they sell every week. He just doesn't get it.

That's why his running analogy had such an impact on

me. I knew God was speaking through my dad to communicate with me in a way I would understand. There's no way my dad could have given this advice on his own knowledge.

He went on, "How much time do you spend researching a shoe before you purchase it? And when you find a pair that you like, do you stay loyal to it, waiting for the new one to come out? Or will you just run in any old pair of shoes?"

"No way!" I said, passionately, "Picking your running shoe is critical to performance. I mean, I have a narrow foot. I can't wear just any shoe that comes in a normal or a wide width. And racing shoes are different from training shoes. Trail running shoes are different. And this!" I said proudly, lifting up my right foot for him to admire my shoes. "This is the best running shoe out there. It's the only one I buy."

"So you consider the terrain too?" he asked. "Of course!"

"Does the distance matter for your pace?" Now, he was smirking a little bit. I hadn't quite figured out where he was going, but he was definitely going somewhere. "If you're going to do a long run, do you start slower than if you're going to do a shorter run?"

"Absolutely. If you start out too fast for a long run, you'll never make it. And if you're too slow for a short run, you won't get a good workout," I shot back. Two could play this "Know-It-All" game.

"Well, all I'm going to tell you is that your life would be a lot smoother if you gave it as much thought and consideration as running."

Yeah, I'm sure that's all he was going to tell me. "Go on," I said. "When you run, you have a plan, and you stick to it—how far you'll run, what you'll wear, how fast you'll go. But in life, Michelle, you try to run a marathon at a 5K pace without stopping to think about the terrain you will come across or what shoes you should wear - which is why half of the time you end up sprinting in stilettos on quicksand."

What? When did he learn what stilettos were? And I don't remember teaching him about pacing....

But he was right.

I began to ask myself some hard questions. Do I give more prayer to life decisions than I give consideration to something as temporary as my daily workout? Do I make "in the moment" decisions without considering how it will impact my future?

Even though I was making significant strides in my spiritual walk, I was still making decisions at a sprinting pace only to discover I couldn't finish the race in my own power. I was burning out every time.

That night, I came across 2 Timothy 4:7 in my reading, *"I have fought the good fight. I have finished the course. I have kept the faith."*

I thought about the start line and the finish line of a race. Do we applaud more for the person who crosses the start line first than we do for anyone who crosses the finish line?

If you've never experienced this, I highly encourage you at some point in your life to go and stand at the finish line of a marathon. Runners come in all shapes and all sizes. They have unique strikes of the foot, individual upper body movements, and of course, they all finish at different times. Some of them cross the finish line without breaking a stride. It seems effortless. Others may struggle with every step. But everyone who completes 26.2 miles has one thing in common: they all finish.

Life is very similar to a race. No one remembers how you started if you don't finish well. We have to live our lives with the end in mind, staying obedient to the work God has called us to do...even if that means temporary discomfort.

God was calling me out of my comfort zone. If I backed out now, I knew it would be deliberate disobedience. The sound of my own voice that had controlled my decision-making was getting softer and softer. Submitting to God's call meant my life as I knew it was over.

While that thought terrified my inner control freak, my core being of rediscovered child-like faith couldn't have been more relieved. The choice I would have thought just months ago would have been so difficult to make was surprisingly easy.

I had to move to Texas. God was in control now.

FOR THOUGHT AND DISCUSSION

1. Has God ever used someone to speak to you for Him on a subject you knew they had no idea what they were talking about? Describe that moment.

2. Do you ever find yourself "sprinting in stilettos on quicksand?" Do you make "in the moment" decisions without considering how it will impact your future? Do you give more prayer to life decisions than you give to temporary things that don't really matter?

3. No one remembers how you started if you don't finish well. How do we live our lives with the end in mind even if that means temporary discomfort?

CHAPTER TEN

———◆———

S O I DID IT.
 I packed up everything and my parents dropped me off at Southwestern Baptist Theological Seminary in Fort Worth, Texas to begin the next chapter of my life. I began working in the admissions office at the seminary and classes started five weeks later.

About three weeks into my new life in Texas, I was about to leave for work when I decided to check my Facebook messages. Since I moved to Texas, Facebook had become both a blessing and a curse. Sure, it was a great way to make sure I stayed in touch with friends from a distance, but the longer I was away from Tennessee and the more fresh faces I met in my new home, that whole "I only accept friend requests from people I know" rule I made when I first set up my account was becoming more fuzzy every day.

James Myers, James Myers, I thought, searching my brain to put a face with the name. Staring at the friend request on the computer screen in front of me was obviously not helping.

I got frustrated when I opened his profile. Why do people put pictures up where you can't see their face? Or choose a picture of them and at least ten other people? Or apparently, if you're gifted enough to be James Myers– both! Seriously, how am I supposed to know which one you are in a faraway shot of you and your buddies white water rafting in helmets?

There were 26,000 students where I did my undergraduate degree. I lived in two major cities in Tennessee growing up and competed in the Miss Tennessee pageant. My dad has served on two megachurch staffs, and now, I work in my seminary's admissions office, where I give tours to prospective students from all over the country five days a week. And I'm supposed to remember everyone? Yeah. I'll get right on that.

"Fine, James Myers," I muttered aloud. "You want to be my friend? You got it. I'm sure I've met you somewhere along the way." Clicking on the "Accept Friend" button, a new window appeared.

"How do you know James Myers?" the screen asked.

Great, now the computer wanted in on the fun of mocking me. I glanced over the choices. Proudly, I dragged the mouse and clicked the box next to, "I don't know."

"Then why are you friends with him?" the next window popped up.

In an over-dramatic fashion, I groaned and banged my head on my desk. "Because if I do know him, I don't want to hurt his feelings!" I objected.

Clicking on the ignore button was somewhat satisfying. "Fine. Be that way," I said, tauntingly. I shook my head, "This keeps getting better. I'm arguing with an inanimate object. And now, I'm talking to myself."

I was about to exit the Internet completely when the mystery man's profile emerged. I began searching for something to jog my memory.

Instead of *something* grabbing my attention, it was *everything*. I scrolled from his interests down to his favorite books, movies and quotes. A cold chill ran down my spine, and an eerie feeling came over me. *He didn't write this*, I thought. *I did.*

I clicked on my homepage to view my profile. The books we listed were almost the same. Our quotes were different, but we cited the same people. "Well, James Myers. I may not know who you are, but you have good taste. At least in books."

The movies were hit or miss. There were a couple of good ones, but he obviously had an obsession with war movies because they were all there. *Braveheart. Gladiator. Troy. We Were Soldiers. Tristan and Somebody.* All good flicks to see. Once. Or when I need a good nap.

I discovered he was from Tennessee. That's a good sign. My chances of knowing him and that I didn't accept a friend request from some psycho stranger were looking up.

The next day, I got a message from James Myers:

Michelle, I was meeting with Dr. Patterson on Tuesday while I was in town and he told me to look you up basically based on the fact that we are from the same state. He did mention that you were Miss Knoxville so I decided to see if you were on here. I was pleased to discover that we do have several things in common besides being from the same state. If this is awkward, feel free not to respond, but if not, I was just curious about some of your experiences at SWBTS. Any words of wisdom? Things like that...James.

This guy was slick, but I saw right through him. He wanted wisdom from a girl who had been here three weeks? Doubtful. I wasn't falling for it. I sent him back a message that was polite, but not personal.

Words of wisdom....you've come to the right place. Being 950 miles away from my family is hard, but it's a lot easier when you know you are in the center of God's will. I've lived here a whopping 3 weeks, and I will begin classes in August.

He didn't back off. He sent another message, and this

time, the last line of it said, "Where do you see yourself in 10 years? 20 years?"

What kind of guy asks that question? Not exactly the, "never met you before, 2nd Facebook message ever" material.

The next day when I got to my office our head ambassador gave each of us student workers a list of new students to call and make sure they had registered for classes.

Guess who was at the top of my list? James Myers.

The "girl" in me flipped out. "It's not my job to call him!" I remember thinking.

Luckily, I didn't have to worry about it for long. The number he listed when he applied was his number from college, and it was no longer a working number. I simply sent him another Facebook message to let him know I had tried to call. If he had any further questions, he could call the admissions office to speak with any student ambassador.

He was smarter than I gave him credit for. He messaged me back with his cell phone number and said he would love to hear from me.

But it still wasn't my job to call him! So I did what any normal girl would do. I sent him a text. That way, he would have my number and be able to call me if he wanted to, but I still wasn't breaking my "I don't call boys" rule.

Well, he did call. Eight hours later, we got off the phone. I had never met him before. He had the thickest southern accent I had ever heard. Thanks to his horrible Facebook profile picture choice, I had no clue what he looked like.

I knew one thing: He feared the Lord and I respected him. I was drawn to James like I had never been drawn to anyone before and I couldn't explain how my heart was changing.

While I sensed that James was bold with his Facebook messages, my senses were confirmed even more during our second marathon phone conversation

Somewhere around 3 a.m., James said, "You know, at this rate, in a few years, we're either going to be best friends... or married."

I froze. Married? The guilt over the potential physical damage anorexia had done to my body rushed over me with just that one word. James insists to this day that I didn't say anything for two minutes. It couldn't have been longer than 30 seconds. Finally, I simply said, "I know."

Our pattern of phone conversations continued throughout the next few weeks. I was not disappointed when I met James in person. His assessment was right. We became best friends very quickly, and it didn't take long for it to develop into something more.

For most of my life I don't think people would have described me as a nurturer and I never really thought I had any of the "mommy" genes. When we were growing up, Melody would beg me to play house and I rarely gave in unless she promised to play rock star with me later.

As I wrote earlier, I was convinced that God's plan for me did not include marriage or children. Coupled with the fact that I knew because of my eating disorder, getting pregnant would be difficult for me and the lack of desire in my heart to be a mom, it seemed logical that God would just want me to be focused on serving Him - not a husband or children. However, even as I shared this with people who asked, I still had a story I couldn't quite shake from my mind...

The summer before 8th grade, I was putting together some family pictures, and I found some pictures of my mom from her young 20's. I'm not afraid to say it - my mom was hot. Terry McNatt did well for himself. Like me, my mom competed in pageants. She only competed at the state level one year because my dad proposed before she could compete again. I showed her the picture, complimented her stunning beauty and asked her, "Do you ever wonder what could have happened if you had gone back to compete again?" She shrugged, "Maybe for a little while...but as soon as we had you girls, I knew that maybe God had created me just for the purpose of being your mom. Someday, I might be a legacy because of you."

I don't think she realized how much those words impacted me. I realized in that moment that God would have to give me a personality transplant in order for me to be a good mother. I wanted the spotlight. I needed the approval of the world. In my mind, it would be failure to say that my life's purpose was for someone else to get the glory. But the stronger my love grew for James, the more my attitude began to change.

James has all the characteristics you could ever want in a father. He's a strong leader, and he seeks the Lord in all areas of his life. He is a natural protector and provider. He leads with such humility that the first time I was ever physically in his presence, I knew I wanted to be his partner in life. Things got even tougher when I realized I had a deep desire to have a family with him someday.

Immediately, my mind drifted to my own mother. I realized then that I had a long way to go. The definition of a servant, my mom always went above and beyond for my sister and me. We had every need met and most of our wants. Whether she was sitting at the table with us to make sure our homework was done or driving us to whatever activity of that season, she was always there. She worked as a teacher and came home to work again - dinner, laundry, cleaning, etc. She did every bit of it without complaining, so much that until I began managing my own house, I didn't recognize how hard she worked.

Up to this point, I had gotten control of the first aspect of my eating disorder. Eating disorders are two-fold: obsessive thoughts and compulsions. I had learned to control most of the critical compulsions. Even though I might feel like restricting my food intake or exercising more than I should, I knew better.

There were other behaviors I adopted that most people wouldn't say were "normal" for a young woman. For example, I knew the mirror lied to me whenever I looked in it. I couldn't trust that what I saw in the mirror was really my reflection. So, I got rid of every full- length mirror I owned. I had a small mirror above my sink in my bathroom, and that was the only one I ever looked in.

As for eating, I was much better than before. However, I still had foods that were "off limits." I was convinced if I ever ate them, I would instantly gain 50 lbs. Just to name a few, I wouldn't touch pork, beef, pasta, or anything that had been cooked in butter.

I remember one day in particular when I came home from working out at the gym. James had finished work early, so he had made chicken tacos. He had gone out of his way to prepare them in a way he thought I would enjoy eating them. Knowing they were healthy, he bought my favorite salsa, light sour cream, and whole wheat tortilla shells. He even bought romaine lettuce to shred instead of iceberg.

But I wasn't there to watch him make the chicken to make sure he hadn't cooked it in butter, and though it was light sour cream, it wasn't fat free. I thanked him, but insisting I wasn't very hungry, I found a can of tomato soup in the pantry and began heating it in the microwave. I was more willing to deal with how uncomfortable and underappreciated I made James feel knowing that I would feel comfortable with my 120-calorie dinner.

James went ahead and sat at the kitchen table as I prepared my "dinner." When I sat down at the table, he looked at me with sad eyes. He didn't raise his voice. He didn't get angry. He just said quietly, "You know, I can't marry you until you get this under control."

Trying not to cry, I looked away. James came over and knelt by my chair, gently turning my face towards his. "Michelle, I love you, but I need you to see this in the big picture. Would you ever want our daughter to go through an eating disorder like yours?"

I shook my head, no longer able to fight the tears back.

"Then, think about the example that you're setting. I don't want our kids to watch the whole family eat one thing while mommy fixes something different. We've got to start having some compromise."

The second phase of my recovery began that night. There was an urgency to get better there that didn't exist with my parents. My parents had to love me...but James didn't. As our relationship deepened, I knew I had to begin making some compromises and releasing some control to James over what I ate. It sounds silly, but I wasn't making the best decisions on my own, and I needed his help.

He didn't go to the opposite extreme, insisting that I eat greasy cheeseburgers and pizza every night. He began making healthier choices for himself. He switched to whole-wheat pasta and leaner cuts of meat. We even discovered that I liked pork tenderloin.

It didn't take long to eliminate the fear in my heart over eating what James cooked. He was on my team. He wanted me to be healthy, and he wanted me to be happy.

I began branching out and adding variety to my diet. My family and friends couldn't believe some of my new favorite foods. (When my brother- in-law discovered that I liked beef jerky, he insisted on calling me "Jerky" for almost a year. Plus, I think I got 15 bags of beef jerky in my stocking at Christmas that year.)

When James and I got married on May 24, 2008, I thought my relationship with food would never be healthier. The compulsions appeared to be gone.

My thought life, however, was a different story. I still battled thinking I was fat. One of the hardest parts of gaining weight, even though I needed to gain weight, was consistent-ly putting clothes on only to discover they didn't fit anymore. It also wasn't safe for me to look in mirrors. I avoided them to the best of my ability.

But at that time, I was pleased to celebrate the victory that even if I had negative thoughts running through my head, I was confident that I would never get back to the point of food restriction.

FOR THOUGHT AND DISCUSSION

————◆————

1. Has God ever taken your life a direction you never thought He would? Explain.

2. Who is the best example of a servant in your life? Do you think people view you as a servant? Why or why not?

3. If you have battled an addiction, who helped you along your way to recovery? Did their care for you help you to realize the selfishness of your actions?

4. If you battled an addiction, did the compulsions disappear before the obsessive thoughts? Explain.

CHAPTER ELEVEN

IN CASE I HAVEN'T ILLUSTRATED MY "CONTROL FREAKNESS" enough for you, allow me to elaborate:

Most people take four years to finish high school and at least another four years to finish college. I finished each in three years.

As I read, I pay attention to grammar and spelling mistakes…even if it's just a Facebook status update. You will never catch me giving 99.9%. I am all… and then some… or nothing.

I usually refer to second place as "first loser."

I insist on mopping my kitchen floor on my hands and knees with a rag. Mops make too much of a mess. Every shirt in my closet is organized by color and sleeve-length.

Before I started keeping my to-do list on my phone, I would rewrite my to-do list several times a day because when I began crossing things off, it looked too messy.

Also, if I think of something I've already done that day, I'll type it and delete it at the same time. Convinced yet? I'm a bit of a perfectionist.

Sure, it's comical. James, who could not be more laid back, makes fun of my Type A+ personality whenever he gets the chance. And while we get a lot of laughs out of my quirks, it can also be serious.

Sometimes, I run myself into the ground trying to keep

up with the expectations I have set for myself as well as the ones that I think others have set for me. I would rather make myself sick than tell someone "no."

I am not alone. Researchers divide perfectionists into three categories:

- **Self-oriented perfectionists**, who expect perfection of themselves. Risk factor: Depression

- **Other-oriented perfectionists**, who demand perfection from other people. Risk factor: Ruined personal relationships

- **Socially prescribed perfectionists**, who think others expect perfection from them. Risk factors: Eating disorders or suicide[14]

I've been all three at various points in my life, and I know I don't want to live like that.

My constant battle of striving for perfection began with good intentions. I must have been in middle school when I highlighted Matthew 5:48 in my Bible, *"You therefore must be perfect, as your heavenly Father is perfect."*

That became my life standard. I wanted to be perfect: perfect student, perfect church member, perfect community volunteer, perfect employee, perfect body.

The pattern continued as I got older, perfect seminary student, perfect wife—perfect pastor's wife, at that. As more roles were piled on my plate, the less perfect I was becoming in every area.

I noticed it in my prayer journal that God was teaching me great lessons, but I never thanked Him in moments where He used me. I spent all of time journaling about what I did wrong and how I would do better next time. (Thank goodness our salvation is a result of two things: God's grace and our faith in Jesus Christ. If salvation came from being a "good person," I would not stand a chance.)

In 2009, six months into our marriage, James and I decided to read through the Bible together using a plan that incorporated both the Old Testament and the New Testament. It didn't take but a few days for me to get to Matthew 5:48. I honestly wanted to skip it.

Instead, I looked at the footnotes in my new ESV Study Bible and read:

"As Christians seek to live in conformity to Scripture, they are in fact pursuing the very perfection of God...all of the Law and the Prophets find their perfect fulfillment in the perfection of the Father, which is what all Jesus' disciples are called to pursue."

It hit me that I had been striving for not only what God defines as perfect, but I wanted to fit the world's definition of perfect, too. From Paul's writing, we know that's impossible: "Am I now trying to win the approval of men, or of God? Or am I trying to please men? If I were still trying to please men, I would not be a servant of Christ." (Galatians 1:10).

I began praying for a perspective change, but it was honestly half- hearted because I didn't really expect anything to change. After all, I'm pretty sure I was high strung by age 6. It seemed like a pointless prayer.

I underestimated God.

The next day, I was reading in Matthew 6 when I stumbled across, *"Do not lay up for yourselves treasures on earth, where moth and rust destroy and where thieves break in and steal, but lay up for yourselves treasures in heaven, where neither moth nor rust destroys and where thieves do not break in and steal. For where your treasure is, there your heart will be also...No one can serve two masters, for either he will hate the one and love the other, or he will be devoted to the one and despise the other. You cannot serve God and money."* (Matthew 6:19-21; 24)

Now I was starting to feel convicted. I began evaluating decisions I made with questions like: What am I trying to prove anyway? Who am I really trying to please? What is my real motivation?

I've been very fortunate to have some extremely godly women in my life. I was sharing what I had learned the past few days with our worship pastor's wife, Elizabeth Parks, when she summed up everything I had been struggling with in just a few simple words:

"Perfection is not the same thing as holiness."

Wow. It's been almost a year since she uttered those words to me, and I've been unpacking that statement ever since. The realizations have gotten more humbling as more time has passed.

It's not enough just to know that I need to strive for holiness instead of perfection. It's the realization that becoming more holy is not a quick fix – it's a process. As if that's not enough, it's not something I can do on my own. It's something God has to do in me.

In *Fire In Your Heart*, Sammy Tippit writes:

"An insight into the holiness of God will always produce a life- style of repentance. When one enters upon this highway called holiness, it does not mean that he is perfect. It does mean that he is walking down a road of change. Repentance means a change of heart or a change of mind. Throughout the Christian life we should be continually changed, or conformed, into the image of Jesus Christ."

Since I started living that truth, I've had a peace inside of me that I'm not sure I ever knew was possible. Leaps of faith that would have seemed impossible to me six months ago have taken place with ease. Conversations that would have previously intimidated me have been effortless.

There's just one secret: I'm not trying to be perfect by my own strength. I'm allowing God to make me more holy in His strength.

I've also found a new verse to strive for in life.

1 Peter 1:16: *"Since it is written, "You should be holy, for I am holy."*

FOR THOUGHT AND DISCUSSION

◆

1. Are you a perfectionist? Using the list at the beginning of this chapter, which type of perfectionist are you?

2. If you are a perfectionist, what are some things you like and dislike about this trait? If you are not a perfectionist, what are some reasons why you wish you were a perfectionist or why are you glad you are not one?

3. Do you think you are striving for what God defines as perfect, what the world defines as perfect, or both?

4. Really unpack this statement: "Perfection is not the same thing as holiness." Make a list to contrast how perfection and holiness are different.

CHAPTER TWELVE

———◆———

I SPENT A LONG TIME REALLY STUDYING AND learning about the character of God. As I examined His attributes in comparison with my human nature, here is what I discovered:

He is supreme. I am dependent on Him.
He is holy. I am sinful.
He is pure. I am corrupt.
He is true. I am deceitful.
He is righteous and just. I am immoral and undeserving.
He responds to unholiness with wrath. Sometimes, I don't even notice.
He is unconditional love. I am situationally selfish – loving and hating who and what is convenient for me.
He is goodness. I have a sin nature.
He is gracious. I am disrespectful.
He is merciful. I am heartless.
He is steadfast. I am unstable.
He is spiritual. I am worldly.
He is wisdom. I am foolish.
He is faithful. I am a traitor.
He is peaceful. I am rebellious.
He is perfection. I am flawed.
He is glory. I am shame.

As I've grown in my walk with the Lord, I've turned over nearly every aspect of my life to Him. And up until this last year, I've been okay with that.

But that's not good enough. God doesn't want nearly every aspect of my life. He desires my whole life. Yet, I continually refuse to submit total control over to God.

Looking at the characteristics of God and comparing them with the standards of the world, I have to wonder, what am I really holding onto? Rebellion? Sin? Shame? Why would I consciously do this when I have the opportunity to have a complete new life in Christ? 2 Corinthians 5:17 says, *"Therefore, if anyone is in Christ, he is a new creation. The old has passed away; behold, the new has come."*

Imagine getting a new pair of jeans. They are the perfect shade of denim and actually fit in length, waist and hips (as a female, a practically impossible feat!). In addition to feeling as soft as sweatpants, they are given to you for free.

Your old jeans are about an inch too big in the waist, could stand to have a little more room around the hips and they are only the perfect length with your tallest pair of boots. Not to mention, they have permanent grass stains, a hole in a place that no one would call fashionable and a zipper that only goes up halfway. The next morning, you go to your closet to get dressed for the day. Which pair of jeans would you get? The new ones, of course!

So why am I capable of seeing the obvious choice in this situation, but continue to put on my old life with all of its flaws when Christ has given me the option of Him living through me in new life? Galatians 2:20 says, *"I have been crucified with Christ. It is no longer I who live, but Christ who lives in me. And the life I now live in the flesh I live by faith in the Son of God, who loved me and gave himself for me."* Later, in Galatians 5:24 Paul writes, *"And those who belong to Christ Jesus have crucified the flesh with its passions and desires."* If I haven't turned over all of my personal passions and desires, do I really belong to Christ?

Once again, it was the lyrics to a song that convicted me to my core and led me to repentance. James and I had called the Jeff Johnson Band to come and lead worship for a weekend event with our college students at Fielder Road Baptist Church in Arlington, Texas, where James serves as the young adult's pastor. As Jeff and his band began to play "Ruin Me," the words ran over my soul:

Woe to me, I am unclean - a sinner found in Your presence.
I see you, seated on Your throne –
Exalted, Your Glory surrounds You.
Now, the plans that I have made fail to compare
When I see your glory.

Ruin my life, the plans I have made.
Ruin desires for my own selfish gain.
Destroy the idols that have taken Your place,
'Till it's You alone I live for, You alone I live for.
Holy, holy is the Lord Almighty!
Holy is the Lord!

The song comes from Isaiah 6 where Isaiah sees God sitting on His throne. He is so overwhelmed by God's presence that he realizes how much he truly needs a Savior.

Let that sink in for a moment...Isaiah – one of the greatest prophets of the Old Testament – realizing his shame before Almighty God. Once he saw God's power, his life changed. The plans he had were ruined because Isaiah finally realized how insignificant he was in comparison to the Lord.

In Isaiah 6:8, Isaiah hears the voice of the Lord saying, "Whom shall I send, and who will go for Us?" Isaiah responds, "Here am I. Send me!" Isaiah didn't wait to find out what the assignment was. He didn't see if it conveniently fit with his work schedule. He heard God's voice, and he responded immediately.

A very similar situation happened centuries before. In

Genesis 12:1, God told Abram (later Abraham) to leave his country and his family to go "to the land which I will show you." Genesis 12:4 records that Abram "went forth." He didn't even know where He was going, but he knew he was following the Lord, and that was all that mattered.

As the lyrics of that song pierced my soul, I realized that while I no longer gave into Satan's temptations to restrict food content, I had never relinquished control of my personal appearance to God.

There were still days when the priority of my workout came before my personal time of Bible study and reflection. There were days when I worried more about gaining weight than the genuine prayer concerns of my family and friends.

The hardest one of all...although I knew children were a blessing from the Lord (Psalm 127:3), I often found myself fearful of what pregnancy would do to alter my body.

Why did I value something as fleeting as beauty when the fear of the Lord should be the ultimate goal of a godly woman (Proverbs 31:30)?

So there I was, singing "Ruin Me" along with the band, realizing that I hadn't rid myself of selfish gain and idols in my life. I had to sit down. I didn't mean the words that were coming out of my mouth.

In tears, I prayed a prayer that sounds silly, but I needed to let go of this area of my life, and I needed to be honest before my Father.

"God, I've been so selfish. If I won't make you the Lord of all of my life, then you're not really my Lord at all. God, if the only way you can use me is by ruining my life, then I'm telling you to do it. If you need to remove my security blanket of being fit, do it. I just want to be used by you."

I know it sounds superficial, but I needed to say it. I needed to say to God that He was more important to me. All that mattered in my life was for Him to be able to use me. If He needed to get the "me" part of my life out of the way, I had to be willing to lay it down. I meant every word.

Ironically, the devotional book I was reading at the time led me to Genesis 22. When I sat down to read that evening, I found myself in tears as I related laying down my obsession with my appearance to Abraham sacrificing the life of his son, Isaac.

My tears, though, were not for the fact that I was sacrificing something important to me. Honestly, since I had moved to Texas, exercise wasn't really something I enjoyed. Sure, it was a good stress relief every once in a while, and I liked the results, but I didn't love exercise itself.

I began crying as I pictured myself standing there next to Abraham at my own altar. As he laid his only son down to sacrifice him to God, I could easily see that he was troubled, but his faith and loyalty to God came first. He was going to go through with sacrificing his son because he trusted God.

God stopped him just in time. I watched as Abraham embraced Isaac. God provided a ram for them, so they sacrificed it instead and worshipped God whole-heartedly.

Shamefully, my gaze fell upon my altar. A pink purse sat on top. It was small and insignificant. It was cute on the outside, but the inside was empty. I had just seen what the Lord had done for Abraham, but I couldn't bear the thought of sacrificing it to God. But what if He didn't stop me? Could I really take the risk of not ever getting it back?

My tears were the result of my realization that I had a long way to go in my relationship with the Lord if I valued my appearance on an equal scale with a parent's love for their child.

At first, I wasn't sure if that meant I didn't need to work out ever again. After thinking about it, though, I knew that wasn't healthy either. I didn't need to go to the opposite extreme. I just needed to make sure my priorities were in order and maintain more balance and moderation in my daily routine.

I took a few days off from the gym to process what God was teaching me. After many hours on my knees, I finally came to the conclusion that if God was going to be first, He had to come first. I made a commitment that I would not let myself do anything active until after I had spent quality time with the Lord.

Since I was used to 5 a.m. workouts, this required a major shift in my schedule. I had a regimen that I rarely veered from. This regimen included getting to the gym 30 minutes before a 5:30 a.m. class so I could run on the treadmill. On Monday, Wednesday, and Fridays I either taught or attended an indoor cycling class and on Tuesdays, Thursdays, and Saturdays I took a strength training class. On Sundays, I would wait until James fell asleep watching football before taking off for a jog around our neighborhood.

I expected the first few days to be tough but I found just the opposite to be true. When I began my day by spending time with God, I found myself thinking about what He had shown me throughout my day. In place of incessantly counting calories, I was spending more time treasuring His truth.

Inside and outside of the church, I'd always heard, "You reap what you sow."[15] But now, the words I was reading in the Bible were consuming my thought life. The Spirit was pushing Satan's lies out of my head.

I memorized Philippians 4:8 to commit to giving God control over my thoughts, "Finally, brothers, whatever is true, whatever is honorable, whatever is just, whatever is pure, whatever is lovely, whatever is commendable, if there is any excellence, if there is anything worthy of praise, think about these things."

It was becoming harder and harder for me to enjoy working out now that I wasn't as consistent in my routine at the gym. I didn't have a set time or schedule and simply went whenever I could fit it in. Often, that meant I didn't arrive at a time when there were classes on the schedule so I was left to fend for myself.

I realized I enjoyed the camaraderie of exercise much more than the actual activity itself. I had convinced myself that I loved running but what I really loved was that my best friend was a runner. Running allowed us to spend time together. Now that my best friend several states away and not really knowing what else to do on my own at the gym, I headed straight for the "dreadmill." Each time I got on that machine it was like I was taking a step back into my old life. However, I still did it claiming it was for balance and moderation, never even admitting to anyone that I truly detested every second of it. But that was all about to change.

Praise the Lord that we serve a God who exists even in the smallest details of our lives.

FOR THOUGHT AND DISCUSSION

———————◆———————

1. Re-read the list comparing God's attributes with human nature at the beginning of this chapter. Did anything on the list stand out to you?

2. Remembering the analogy of that perfect pair of jeans, why do you think we would obviously choose to wear the new jeans, but continue to live in our old life apart from Christ instead of being a new creation?

3. Even if you have recovered from an addiction, have you fully turned it all over to God? Would giving it up ruin your life? Are you willing to let your life be ruined if that is what God chooses to do?

4. In the overall picture of life, how important is your addiction? Is your addiction as important as Abraham's son that he was willing to sacrifice because God asked him to, or it is more like the pink purse on my altar?

5. List your top five priorities. Now, list the first five things you do each day. (Yes, you can start after brushing your teeth.) How would your day look different if you began each day with your top priority?

CHAPTER THIRTEEN

O NE TUESDAY MORNING IN SEPTEMBER OF 2008, I woke up and spent time with the Lord. Knowing I had a day of studying ahead of me, I decided to go to the gym before heading to the library.

As I walked up the stairs, it was like my legs were fighting me. I couldn't bear the thought of those scary years of my life where I practically lived on a treadmill.

When I reached the top of the stairs, I looked back and forth between the elliptical machines, the stair climbers, the rows of bikes, and the free weights. I was starting to walk toward the weights when I heard music blast from behind me.

I whipped around to the group exercise room behind me. The room was packed and they all seemed to be a part of some club. Their outfits all looked alike and it was not your typical workout wear.

Why are there straps hanging from their shorts? Why do most of them have on tube socks? Ooh! I want her hat!

Thoughts ran through my mind but in the midst of all of that, one thing stood out even more. Everyone in the room had a huge smile on their face. *Didn't they know they were working out? Where were the grunts and groans of pain and agony?*

Suddenly, I realized that I was hovering around the door

so as an attempt to remain unnoticed I started to walk away, but it was too late.

The instructor saw me. She hollered, "Hey, you! Cute little blonde thing! Get yourself in here!" Then, she went right back to cuing the class without missing a beat.

I hesitated. In addition to their own wardrobe, this class seemed to have its own vocabulary. She was cuing moves I had never heard of before.

The instructor looked over at me again. This time, she made a big waving motion at me, flashing a huge smile.

Tentatively, I walked in and fell into step with the ener-gized group. I kicked. I danced. I punched. I yelled. I sang the lyrics back when she pointed at the class. I laughed so much that it hurt. I learned the class was called TurboKick, which was a fusion of kickboxing and hip-hop dance.

My form was terrible. I went left when the rest of the group went right. They knew when to clap and when to hold, and I never seemed to get it right. I was sweating and it didn't take long for me to feel physically exhausted, but I was having a blast.

An hour passed, but it felt like it couldn't have been more than five minutes. At the end of the class, I went up and in-troduced myself to the instructor, Mindy Lawhorne. I told her that I was an instructor but that I was in school and had another job so I wasn't teaching very much.

"You're an instructor?" she asked, "I was praying God would send me someone else for my next certification. Thank you, Jesus! You've got to get certified to teach this. You'll love it!" Dumbfounded at the mention of Jesus at the gym, I took the information she handed me and walked to my car.

Once I got to my car, the tears fell as I had three realiza-tions hit me all at once. First, I was hungry. While running seemed to suppress my appetite, that was not the case with this class. I was ready for food. Second, I realized that hour class was the first time I had worked out when I felt like I wasn't punishing myself for eating.

Though I love them all dearly, this is not a universal endorsement for TurboKick (or the in-home version TurboJam) or 24 Hour Fitness, where I first participated in this format. Everyone is different. (Although, if you're funky and fun, love to dance, and secretly wish you were Jack Bauer's crime fighting CTU partner on 24, you, like me, may find this to be your "soulmate" workout.)

However, this is an endorsement of a God who is big enough to part the Red Sea to allow the Israelites to escape safely from the Egyptian army[16], to send a chariot of fire to retrieve His prophet Elijah[17] and to shut the mouths of the lions in Daniel's den.[18] This very same God is small enough to notice my tears of frustration at the gym and provide me with an outlet to form a healthy relationship with exercise, a new sister in Christ and an unconventional avenue to share Him with a lost world...by attending one group exercise class.

I know some of you must be thinking that you can't believe I am wasting time in my book to mention this. If it ended there, I would agree that this is a relatively insignificant detail. But it doesn't.

When I took Mindy's class, I had already been teaching group exercise classes for five years and while some of my class participants knew of my involvement in church and seminary, I doubt most people knew the value I placed on my walk with Christ. My gym life and my church life were completely separate.

Even before Mindy told me she had been praying for me and praised Jesus in our conversation, I knew she believed in Jesus with her whole heart. You don't get the kind of joy that was reflected in her face (especially after several minutes of lunges!) from anything in this world. After we became close friends and I shared this with her, Mindy lit up. "That is my favorite part about teaching! People continually ask me where my energy comes from. When they're waiting on me to shout out some magic energy drink, I simply get to say, 'His name is Jesus.'"

That was when the call on my life started to come together. If you were to look at my life's course up until that day, you would think I had my left foot on the fitness road and my right foot on the Jesus road. Seriously, I know my résumé looks funny, it's split right down the middle. With the exception of my pharmaceutical sales job, I've either worked for Christian organizations or a gym.

My conversation with Mindy sparked me to begin to pray for opportunities to share the joy that can only come from a personal relationship with Jesus in places where it was unexpected - namely, at the gym.

No one knows better than I do that if you want to find selfishness, one of the primary places to check is the gym. I've got first-hand experience in that department. Sure, you find people there whose primary concern is health, but you will likely also be able to find those who are self- absorbed.

Personally, my Christianity was probably least expressed at the gym. Burning calories was my only mission. Jesus was on a different schedule. But in Matthew 5:13-16, Jesus encourages believers to use their lives to influence others for good. We have the opportunity to be living testimonies of how the Lord has changed our lives. Considering my past struggles, what better place for the Lord to put me to be salt and light for Him than in the fitness industry itself?

Matthew 9:37-38 says, "Then He [Jesus] said to His disciples, "The harvest is plentiful, but the workers are few. Therefore, beseech the Lord of the harvest to send out workers into the harvest."

Growing up with a father in ministry and now married to a pastor, I had never really experience what it's like to live life when your family works outside the realm of ministry. I've spent so much time in each of the churches where they both served that I'm sure I could walk through the buildings blindfolded and give a detailed description of what I was passing.

I've taught Sunday school, children's choir, youth Bible study and women's discipleship groups. I've been a member of church choirs, praise teams and the youth orchestra (though I'm not sure my flute playing even qualified as a "joyful noise"). I've made phone calls to visitors, written articles for church magazines, changed diapers in the nursery, stacked chairs, decorated the atrium for holidays, washed communion dishes and counted heads on youth camp buses.

And I know I'm not alone. I know many brothers and sisters in Christ who probably can't name two roles of service at the church they haven't participated in at one point in their life.

First of all, let me say that serving God inside His house has always been and will always be an important part of my life. It is my personal conviction to never be a "benchwarmer" at my church and I always want to be active in at least one of my church's ministries.

I was now beginning to realize that my personal fitness could be a critical part of my witness. As I read those verses in Matthew, I couldn't help but think, "When Jesus talked about the harvest, he wasn't just talking about serving the church."

How do I serve God by my interactions with my family?
How do I serve God at my job?
How do I serve God in the city where I live?
How do I serve God with the way I treat people He puts in my life?

The harvest Jesus is talking about is much bigger than the walls of our churches. I began to pray for God to open up opportunities in my life to go into the harvest, which he has done over and over again. I prayed that above the quality of my workout, above my cardiovascular threshold that God would simply give me the endurance to continually spread

His joy among people I come across at the gym. Whether that means planting a seed in a non-believer, actually getting to share my faith, or simply being able to encourage a co-laborer in Christ, I just want to be used by God wherever He places me.

Since praying that prayer, I've met other women at the gym who have experienced body image struggles and full-blown eating disorders. I've had opportunities to pray with women experiencing tough times, such as a best friend's battle with cancer, the loss of a husband's job, or the horrific pain of burying a child.

I've also gotten to rejoice with them as they uncover new truths about their Savior, they watch their child get baptized, or they simply take the first step by agreeing to visit my church with me.

Finally, my life was starting to come together. God wasn't asking me to choose between serving Him and working in fitness. He was calling me to use my passion for fitness to bring Him glory. I adopted a work mission statement from one of my mentors, Jackie Bull, who shares a similar calling: "Fitness is my witness."

Here's the major difference though… once upon a time, I would desire to know every detail of exactly how God planned to use me. Now, I just take it day by day, striving to respond in obedience to His direction.

I finally understand what it means to be free in Christ. Freedom in Christ comes when you stop compartmentalizing your Christianity and give full control to Christ. This attitude of, *I'll control this, God, but you can have that part of my life. I'll behave this way at church, God, but when I'm somewhere else, that's my territory,* that's a hard life to live.

Releasing full control of your entire life to the God who saved you - letting the Lord use you wherever you are, behaving like the same person whether you're at a ballgame or a Bible study, conducting a group exercise class or a business meeting, sitting in a room full of infants, executives, close friends or total strangers - that's not losing control of your life. That's freedom in Christ!

I wonder if the Holy Spirit is challenging you as he challenged me with these verses. Could you start a Bible study among your co-workers? Could you create a prayer group with ladies in your neighborhood? Would you just have an open evening in your schedule so you could have a family who is struggling financially over for dinner?

My prayer for anyone who is reading these words is the same prayer that I pray for myself. I pray that we would be open to the Spirit's leading, wherever God would call us to serve - whether inside or outside of the church. One thing can be certain: There is plenty of work to be done. I desire to be one of the workers, and I faithfully pray for God to send more.

FOR THOUGHT AND DISCUSSION

1. Have you ever met someone outside of church that reflected Jesus so much that you instantly knew they were a Christian? Describe their behavior and your interaction with them.

2. Do you think someone could have answered the first question with a story about you? Why or why not?

3. What are some of your favorite stories in the Bible that reflect how big and powerful our God is?

4. Do you believe the same God is small enough to care about the seemingly insignificant details of your life? Why or why not?

5. If you have overcome an addiction, are you willing to allow God to use you as a living testimony for the change He has done in your life? Has he already done it? If so, how?

6. List some ways you serve God inside the church.

7. List some ways you serve God outside of the church.

8. Freedom in Christ comes when we stop compart-mentalizing our Christianity and give full control to Christ. Do you agree with this statement? Why or why not?

9. Where do you feel like God is calling you to serve Him?

CHAPTER FOURTEEN

———◆———

Almost immediately after James proposed, the most frequently asked question I got changed from, "When do you think y'all will get married?" to, "When do you want to start having kids?" Now that we've been married a year and a half, it's hard to experience one day without that question.

Almost every time I hear it, guilt and shame washes over me. Sure, not everyone knows my past. Or maybe they do and just don't realize having an eating disorder like mine does plenty of irreversible damage to your reproductive system. It's a daily prayer to give that lingering burden in my life over to God to bear for me.

Every now and then, reality hits: What if I can't give this amazing man the biological children that he deserves?

Over the past year, we've seen several of our couple friends become parents. It has sparked conversations between us about the names of our children, adoption, and how we think our parents will handle being grandparents from a distance.

One day amidst dreaming about the future, we decided on at least one name for a boy and a girl. Our little boy will be Noah, and our little girl will be Storie. (No offense to Nicholas Sparks, but Noah is named after the Noah from the Bible, not from *The Notebook*. Storie's name has no meaning other than, "My mom's a writer.")

After our conversation that day, it became easier to pray for these little ones by name. For someone who didn't have a desire to be a mom until three years ago, I must be making up for lost time. I am already crazy in love with my kids... and they aren't even on their way yet!

Somehow, in my prayers, my children became real. They became so real that even though they aren't physically with us on this earth yet, they've done something that only God could orchestrate: They got rid of every trace of an eating disorder in me - my thought life included.

I never thought I would be able to go a day without making sure that my daily calorie intake was equivalent or less than my daily calories burned. I never thought I would be able to look in a mirror and see what everyone else sees when they look at me. I never thought I would ever experience a day of complete freedom of eating when I felt hungry and stopping when I was satisfied.

But I can.

After we named our kids, I started a pattern. If I ever had an anorexic thought, I began praying for Noah and Storie. Seeing their sweet faces in my imagination just made me smile and put my mind where it needs to be - off of myself and on the responsibility of taking care of my family.

This past year on Mother's Day, I was not able to celebrate as a mom, but I was able to celebrate my precious Noah and Storie, who have helped their mother more than they'll ever know. I can't believe that I ever allowed myself to be so inward focused that I could think that raising a child was a wasteful legacy. I am eager to see how God uses the lives of Noah and Storie to do His work. I can honestly utter the same words that my mother said to me in the 8th grade and mean them with my whole heart: If my legacy on this earth is being known as the mother of Noah and Storie Myers, I accept that responsibility with the greatest joy.

I wish that I could end this book with the joyful news that I'm pregnant. If this were a movie of God's total healing and restoration, I'm sure that's how it would end. However, that's not the case. This isn't a movie, and I'm not pregnant.

But I'm hopeful, and I know that I will be a mother someday.

I don't know if motherhood will come to me through natural birth or adoption - but for now, I pray the prayer of Hannah:

"I am the woman who was standing here in your presence, praying to the Lord. For this child I have prayed and the Lord has granted me my petition that I made to him. Therefore I have lent him to the Lord. As long as he lives, he is lent to the Lord." (1 Samuel 1:26b-28)

FOR THOUGHT AND DISCUSSION

◆

1. If you have previously battled an addiction, do you still experience guilt and shame for your past sin?

2. Are there still consequences or unanswered questions lingering from a past addiction? What are they, and how do you handle them?

3. Romans 12:2 says, "And do not be conformed to this world, but be transformed by the renewing of your mind, that you may prove what is that good and acceptable and perfect will of God." What are some ways you can renew your mind to rid yourself of any leftover temptation, guilt or shame from your addiction?

CHAPTER FIFTEEN

---◆---

PRAYING FOR MY CHILDREN WAS DEFINITELY THE FINAL turning point in my eating disorder. It helped me realize my mindset was the most important thing about my relationship with food that needed to change. Since that discovery, I've made so many positive lifestyle adjustments that my family and I don't even refer to me during those years of my life as Michelle. We call her "Anna" (not too original, I know.)

Every person is unique. Every person's struggle, even with a similar addiction, will look different. Nevertheless, I'd like to leave you with five modifications I made to my daily rituals to help me leave my addiction in my past.

I started counting my blessings instead of counting calories. If I ever pull out an old notebook, or even a textbook that I've owned since I was in college, I will frequently find pages of assorted numbers added in the margins. I was obsessed with knowing exactly how many calories were going into my body. Sometimes, I would calculate my intake several times a day. I couldn't take a chance on making an error in the numbers.

This was a difficult habit to break. Even if I could restrain myself from writing it down, I would find myself calculating calories as I pulled items out of the refrigerator to prepare a meal.

I have made a habit of reading Deuteronomy 8:1-10. Though the words were intended for the Israelites, they speak to me as if I had been right there wandering with them in the wilderness:

"All the commandments that I am commanding you today you shall be careful to do, that you may live and multiply, and go in and possess the land which the LORD swore to give to your forefathers. You shall remember all the way which the LORD your God has led you in the wilderness these forty years, that He might humble you, testing you, to know what was in your heart, whether you would keep His commandments or not. *He humbled you and let you be hungry, and fed you with manna which you did not know, nor did your fathers know,* that He might make you understand that *man does not live by bread alone, but man lives by everything that proceeds out of the mouth of the LORD.* Your clothing did not wear out on you, nor did your foot swell these forty years. Thus you are to know in your heart that the LORD your God was disciplining you just as a man disciplines his son. Therefore, you shall keep the commandments of the LORD your God, to walk in His ways and to fear Him. For the LORD your God is bringing you into a good land, a land of brooks of water, of fountains and springs, flowing forth in valleys and hills; *a land of wheat and barley, of vines and fig trees and pomegranates, a land of olive oil and honey; a land where you will eat food without scarcity, in which you will not lack anything;* a land whose stones are iron, and out of whose hills you can dig copper. *When you have eaten and are satisfied, you shall bless the LORD your God* for the good land which He has given you."
- Deuteronomy 8:1-10

Anytime anyone in the medical field hears my story, they are amazed I am alive. Most people who restrict their food like I did, coupled with pushing their bodies to physical limits, die fairly quickly. Just as God provided nourishment for the Israelites as they wandered in the wilderness for their disobedience, God sustained my life above what science says should have been the outcome of my situation.

Whenever I think about counting calories, I begin to reflect on everything I have to be thankful for. Of course, I start with the big things, like my husband and the amazing students in the college ministry at our church. Some days, that's enough. On harder days, I feel like I thank God for everything from my niece's giggle to ultra-fine Sharpies.

Plus, if I ever find doodling numbers of consumed calories in the margins, I quickly pull out a card and begin writing a note of encouragement or thanks to someone who needs it. This helps me to put my mind off of my selfish insecurities and hopefully ensure security in someone else.

I live each day guided by the promise that God pulled me through for a purpose. Going back to a lifestyle of counting calories belittles my Creator's intentions for my life.

I scaled back my wardrobe. Initially, as I struggled to get back to a normal weight, I thought it made sense to weigh myself regularly to make sure that I was making progress. I found the exact opposite to be true.

Each time I stepped on the scale, my worst fear was coming true. I was gaining weight. I could already feel my clothes getting tighter, which was hard enough. Seeing the numbers only made it worse. It seemed to be an automatic reflex for me. Once the numbers started going up on the scale, panic set in, and I immediately wanted to either go work out or skip a few meals.

Getting dressed in the morning was getting harder. It seemed every outfit I put on didn't fit right anymore. Granted, these were the pants that I had altered smaller than a size zero. They didn't NEED to fit me anymore, but that didn't change that it was difficult to continually put on clothes that were getting too small.

After several weeks of tears and finally deciding on a pair of sweatpants and a t-shirt I could wear, I cleaned out almost everything in my closet. It was my way of committing to never be that size again.

I thought having less clothes to choose from would be a huge hassle. After all, I still wanted to look nice (what girl doesn't?). However, having less to choose from ultimately helped me focus less on my appearance. Romans 12:2 reminds believers to not conform to the patterns of this world so focusing less on my appearance seemed to be a good start.

I seek to please God with my heart more than I seek to please the world with my appearance. 1 Samuel 16:7 explains: "Man looks at the outward appearance, but the Lord looks at the heart."

Obviously, this is not referring to the muscle that pumps blood throughout the body, but to the soul and reflection of Christ within us as believers. 1 Kings 8:39 says that God is the only one who knows the hearts of all mankind. The Lord even goes as far as to search "all hearts and understands every intent of the thoughts" (1 Chronicles 28:9).

To me, being beautiful in God's eyes involves knowing His word, keeping His commands, and demonstrating love, wisdom, purity, gentleness, compassion and humility. When I think of these traits I can't help but see smiles, joy and laughter. A woman possessing a personality like this will radiate these traits because her heart is so full of God that it can't help but manifest itself on the outside in some way. Proverbs 15:13 says, a joyful heart is always accompanied by a cheerful face. Similarly, Proverbs 27:19 reads, "As water face reflects face, so the heart of man reflects man." Several women in the Bible are described as beautiful in physical appearance, yet we rarely come across descriptions of their long, flowing hair or their piercing green eyes. Their actions coincide with the attributes of a beautiful heart.

For example, Rebekah was described as, "very beautiful, a virgin" and immediately exhibited a servant's heart to a thirsty Isaac (Gen 24:14, 18). Purity, gentleness, and compassion accentuated her lovely features.

Esther was likewise described as, "beautiful of form and face." She was also a virgin and predominantly modeled obedience to keeping God's commands, even when faced with the possibility of losing her own life (Est 2:7; 4:16).

Sarai, the wife of Abraham, was recognized as beautiful and Peter used her as an example of modeling godly living with her behavior (Gen 12:11; 1 Pet 3:6).

Ultimately, my goal is not to strive to be like Esther, Rebekah or Sarai. They may have been great women, but they were imperfect just as I am. Instead, my focus is on Christ. He is the only one who possessed these heart traits in their entirety.

Maya Angelou said it this way, "A woman's heart should be so hidden in Christ that a man must be seeking the Lord to find it." Of course, she was referring to a romantic relationship, but the principle applies to a Christian woman's life in general. We should live our lives in such a way that in order to grasp the depths of our beauty, one must first understand the magnificence of the God we serve.

One morning when I was struggling more than most, God comforted me with this thought: "Michelle, when you look in a mirror, I don't want you to see yourself through your eyes. I want you to see yourself through My eyes." Now, I feel most beautiful when I am serving willingly and cheerfully, reflecting Christ with my actions and telling others about Him.

I switched the focus of my discipline to godliness. Paul's letters in the New Testament contain some of my favorite reading material. As an athlete, I identify with Paul. He speaks my language. "Everyone who competes in the games goes into strict training. They do it to get a crown that will not last; but we do it to get a crown that will last forever. Therefore I do not run like a man running aimlessly; I do not fight like a man beating the air. No, I beat my body and make it my slave so that after I have preached to others, I myself will not be disqualified for the prize" (1 Corinthians 9:25-27).

Between the running and boxing references, this verse couldn't feel more personal to me. Paul is saying, "Training for athletic competition is fun...but it's temporary. The Gospel is the only thing worthy of our eternal focus."

He spelled the same concept out plainly for Timothy. Paul writes, "Have nothing to do with godless myths and old wives' tales; rather, train yourself to be godly. For physical training is of some value, but godliness has value for all things, holding promise for both the present life and the life to come" (1 Timothy 4:7-8).

Paul doesn't belittle exercise. He simply offers a priority perspective. Training and disciplining ourselves to be godly is more important than our 5K time, how many push-ups we can do, or what size dress we fit in.

So, what does training for godliness look like? For me, it means studying His word daily, worshipping loudly in my car, praying continuously throughout my day and showing His love to others. It means serving in the local church, reaching out to my community, building accountability with other believers and developing intentional friendships with those who do not know Him.

There are so many ways we can give God glory with our lives. Anything we do that seeks to spend more time with our Father is training for godliness and disciplining ourselves to be His servants.

I will never be able to fully comprehend the value that God places on me, but I'm trying. The best perspective I can grasp is knowing that my husband's love for me—I know he loves me as much as any human is physically capable of loving another human—pales in comparison to how much God loves me.

In Jesus' longest recorded sermon, The Sermon on the Mount, He said:

"Therefore I tell you, do not worry about your life, what you will eat or drink; or about your body, what you will wear. Is not life more important than food, and the body more important than clothes? Look at the birds of the air; they do not sow or reap or store away in barns, and yet your heavenly Father feeds them. Are you not much more valuable than they? Who of you by worrying can add a single hour to his life? And why do you worry about clothes? See how the lilies of the field grow. They do not labor or spin. Yet I tell you that not even Solomon in all his splendor was dressed like one of these. If that is how God clothes the grass of the field, which is here today and tomorrow is thrown into the fire, will he not much more clothe you, O you of little faith? So do not worry, saying, 'What shall we eat?' or 'What shall we drink?' or 'What shall we wear?' For the pagans run after all these things, and your heavenly Father knows that you need them. But seek first his kingdom and his righteousness, and all these things will be given to you as well." (Matthew 6:25-33)

Have you ever climbed a tall mountain or stood on top of the Empire State Building? Even though I'm afraid of heights, I've done both. Each time, I coached myself, "Don't look down."

We need to take the same advice with the challenges and temptations we face in our Christian walk. Instead of looking at our past, listening to temptation or worrying about the next time we will mess up, we simply need to look up, putting our every focus on our Savior.

Romans 8:37-39 says, "No, in all these things we are more than conquerors through him who loved us. For I am convinced that neither death nor life, neither angels nor demons, neither the present nor the future, nor any powers, neither height nor depth, nor anything else in all creation, will be able to separate us from the love of God that is in Christ Jesus our Lord."

No addiction is too big for God to overcome. I love Paul's words here. When we rely on the love of God that is in Christ Jesus to lead our lives, no hardship is even a close match for our God. Through Him, we are more than conquerors.

I allow God to define my beauty - not the world. In Matthew 15:8, Jesus quotes the prophet Isaiah in a discussion with the Pharisees: "These people honors me with their lips, but their heart is far from Me; in vain do they worship Me, teaching as doctrines the commandments of men."

I lived in that trap for too long. I knew the right answers I was supposed to say while I was at church or around other believers. Yet, I let the condition of the world have a greater impact on my life than the teachings of God - the very same world that seeks to condition me to believe that our society used to be too conservative. But now, we've evolved. We've changed with times. Things that were once unacceptable are now okay. I should go ahead and let loose. Live a little!

While times may change, God does not. No matter how much applause I get from people on this earth, it never fills the void of my deepest desire to have the approval of the One who created me.

Though I love getting dressed up, trying new beauty products and dressing up jeans and a t-shirt with funky accessories as much as the next female, I try to remind myself often that the only thing really worth beautifying is who I am on the inside. "That of your inner self, the unfading beauty of a gentle and quiet spirit, which is of great worth in God's sight." (1 Peter 3:4). According to God, none of my physical features define my beauty in His eyes.

After all, "Charm is deceptive, and beauty is fleeting; but a woman who fears the LORD is to be praised" (Proverbs 31:30). Even Dr. 90210 cannot pause the hands of time.

Everything that's lifted now will eventually sag. No amount of Botox will be able to control the wrinkles forever.

On days when I find myself being too consumed with what the world sees on the outside, here's imagery I use to remind myself how God sees us:

Imagine your Creator forming you in your mother's womb. He gets excited as He decides on every feature. He gives you your father's dimples, your mother's hair, and even throws in your grandmother's smile. He knows that when she dies when you're only 8-years-old, that smile will comfort your mother in her mother's absence. He gives you a dose of determination, even though He knows that will undoubtably manifest itself frequently in the form of stubbornness. He thinks about your life with a smile as He makes the finishing touches, such as the lives you will touch and how He will use you.

He also knows you will have moments where you will disobey Him. He'll guide you in the way you should go, and you'll defiantly turn against Him. But each time you return to His loving arms, expressing your regret, He'll hold you like you never left...just like He's holding you now.

And though it happens every time He creates one of His children, it never gets old. Each child He creates has a unique purpose, a hope, and a future. He thinks about how much He loves you in those few precious moments He has with just you...before anyone else even knows you exist.

Whenever I'm challenged to value things that are superficial, such as my looks, I fight the urge to be plastic and pray for God to perform surgery on my heart to align it with His. As Deuteronomy 30:6 says, "The LORD your God will circumcise your hearts and the hearts of your descendants, so that you may love him with all your heart and with all your soul, and live."

If you forget everything you read in this book, I encourage you to take this last thought with you. Would your life be different if you began each day with the following statement?

"Today, I will not be consumed with me. I will not just exist in this world. I'm going to truly live for Him."

FOR THOUGHT AND DISCUSSION

1. Review the five steps in this chapter. If you battled an addiction other than an eating disorder, what are five things you can do to proactively change your old behaviors?

2. What does it mean to you to not just exist in this world but truly live for God? How would it change your life if living for Him was your main focus?

PURPOSE IN PAIN

Babies

Almost six years have passed since I wrote the words in the last chapter. I remember quoting Mark 9:24 out loud as I typed the words, thinking of my future children: "I do believe! Help my unbelief!"

Just a few weeks after writing those words, I would find out the beginning of God's redemptive plan: I was pregnant.

In true dramatic fashion, I actually found out I was pregnant at my first official doctor's appointment regarding infertility. I put off that appointment for four months longer than what is recommended for couples who have been trying to get pregnant without success.

It wasn't that I didn't want to take needed steps toward having children. It was simply that I was afraid of confirmation of my greatest fear: that nothing could be done for us. The damage from my sin was medically irreversible.

But our amazing God had a different plan.

Our insurance required a negative pregnancy test on file in the doctor's office to be approved for treatment. That was the first order of business.

The sweet nurse could sense my disappointment. "You don't need to wait for the results," she reassured me. "Just leave it in the bathroom, and I'll come back to get it for you."

So I left the pregnancy test in the bathroom as quickly as possible, my heart not wanting to see negative appear. I anxiously waited for the doctor.

She walked in with multiple bags and a few stacks of paperwork. I took a deep breath as an attempt to prepare myself for her instructions to follow next.

She waved one stack of papers in front of me. "Well, this is what I had prepared for you prior to your arrival – options, testing for you, testing for you husband... But this is what you're leaving with. These are our new mommy materials. You're pregnant!"

I just stared at her. I'm honestly not sure how long, but long enough for her to come over to me and grip my shoulder. And that's when the tears fell.

When I could finally muster words, I said, "Are you sure that test was mine?"

"I'm sure," she said, laughing. "But you can take another one if you'd like and see for yourself."

So I did. And for the first time, I watched a positive sign pop up on a pregnancy test.

Oh, the goodness of our God!

My pregnancy was relatively uneventful until I started spotting at 32 weeks. I hadn't had any bleeding, so I did my best not to be concerned.

But thankfully, after a sleepless night spent crying out to Jesus for my little boy, I declared March 17 as "Pray for Noah Jackson Day" on my blog. Around noon, we were able to get into my doctor's office for a check-up. After a stress test, I relaxed immediately after hearing Noah's heartbeat.

But the doctors were still concerned and sent me across the street to the hospital for further review.

Noah was born via emergency C-section after I had an unexplained placental abruption. He came eight weeks earlier than his scheduled arrival.

Later, we found out 30 minutes would have made a difference in his life. Needless to say, I can't wait to see the plans God has for my little boy who defied medicine twice to be with us.

The whole ordeal was quite a blur. I don't remember much, except I kept hearing Exodus 14:14 echo in my brain over and over again: "The Lord your God will fight for you; you need only to be still."

What I do remember was eight hours later when I was cleared to move from my room to go visit Noah in the NICU.

I caught a glimpse of him in the incubator. At 4 lbs. 5 oz., he was so tiny. We weren't allowed to hold him yet since he was unable to regulate his body temperature on his own. But I stuck my hand through one of the side openings, and instinctively, Noah reached out his little hand for mine.

Every moment I had waited was worth it.

Every waiting moment when I desired him and doctors told me, "No."

Every waiting moment when I prayed for him and God said, "Wait."

Every waiting moment after taking a pregnancy test only to see the word "Negative" come up…over and over again.

Every waiting moment when it seemed everyone around me was pregnant, and I still was unsure if I would ever be called "Mom."

Each and every waiting moment vanished when his tiny hand grabbed mine.

We spent five long weeks in the NICU. Talk about an emotional rollercoaster. There's no joy like becoming a parent for the first time. And there's also no fear like watching that child you love so much fight for their life.

But despite his scary start, Noah is a strong, vibrant five-year-old. You would never know his early struggles by looking at him.

Our next two children don't have near as dramatic tales, but they are still every bit as miraculous. Cole was born about two and a half years after Noah, and I'm currently halfway through my third pregnancy with our first girl. We can't wait to meet our sweet Shea!

Parenting is nothing as I imagined; it's both harder and better. When I called my dad to tell him I was pregnant with Noah, he made me two promises: "You will never pray the same, and you will never sleep the same."

And as usual, he was right.

I don't deserve these sweet lives to influence. But that's what makes them gifts of grace. As my pastor says, "Mercy is simply not getting what you deserve, but grace is getting what you don't deserve."

So whether your story ends like mine or not, look for His grace. It's there. I've met several strong Christian women who have similar stories of painful pasts with anorexia. We don't all have the same ending to our journeys, but there is one familiar thread that remains: God's grace is evident. His grace is enough. And His grace is everything.

The lives of my sweet children would be enough redemption. But God didn't stop there. He answered my prayers to bring further purpose from my pain. He wasn't done yet.

Cross Training Couture

AFTER NOAH WAS BORN, I CONTINUED WORKING IN home fitness. But I kept feeling like God had more. Just before Noah turned two, God reminded me of an idea He had laid on my heart during my recovery: faith-based fitness tanks.

I had the first few designs in my head, so I called a friend who is a graphic designer and asked her if she would help me get what was in my head on paper. Just a few days later, the first designs were complete.

My sweet husband wasn't unsupportive...but he was hesitant. After all, I already had one job and a baby. He didn't understand how this wouldn't overwhelm me. But he lovingly agreed to help me arrange all the details. He gave me appropriate boundaries that wouldn't allow this project to consume me, but would still allow me to be obedient to what I felt God calling me to do.

But he was firm: No inventory. No website. Pre-orders only.

In his words, he wanted me to be able to get this "heart project" out of my system without getting discouraged if others weren't as excited as I was, or without doing work that wouldn't prove to be necessary.

But after two rounds of pre-orders and more designs that kept coming into my mind, even James could see it:

God was up to something.

So just like that, Cross Training Couture was born. We managed inventory out of my garage for about 18 months, but we couldn't keep up with the growth. Not only were we running out of room, but we were having to re-order inventory almost every other week to keep up with demand.

It was starting to become pretty time-consuming. Even with help shipping the tank tops from interns and assistants, it was too much to manage. I began to wonder if it was time to close the shop until my kids were in school and I had more time to manage the ministry's demands.

That same week, God provided a new screen-printer who had a large warehouse space. Not only were they willing to house our line, but they were also willing to ship for us. Not only that, but it wouldn't increase our businesses expenses. Oh, and they are sold out for Jesus too.

I can't make this stuff up. I'm not that good of a writer. Our God is just that detailed and just that good.

The line has been functioning for three years now, and we continue to see Him move. Just this past week, we had customers who tagged us wearing our line at 5K races, moms and kids with matching Easter outfits sporting CTC, and even one sweet woman who chose one of her favorite tanks to wear while she was baptized.

While we'll be able to keep tabs on how many tank tops we've sold, we'll never know how many eyes were able to read God's truth when they saw others wearing our line. I'll never know all the seeds planted, conversations started, or lives encouraged.

But I do know the One who gives the growth, and for that, I am eternally grateful.

She Works His Way

JUST ONE MORE, AND THEN, I'LL WRAP THIS up.

With two businesses and two babies, I was constantly begging God to show me how to do this His way and with excellence. After all, these were not just jobs. They were callings. Working for me was not only a joy, but it was an act of obedience.

Naturally, I found myself surrounded with other women who were caught in this same balancing act of motherhood and purposeful work.

Over time, God began showing me that it wasn't really about balance. Balance means that all things in life have equal importance. I began to realize I was going about this struggle all wrong.

God doesn't call us to lead balanced lives. He calls us to lead fully surrendered lives. His way means living in complete surrender to Him first, and trusting Him to order everything else accordingly.

Matthew 6:33 reminds us, "But seek first His Kingdom and His righteousness, and all these things will be added to you as well."

For several days in a row during my quiet time, I heard God's still, small voice whisper, "She Works His Way."

So I founded a community for working women who desire that surrendered over balanced life. God alone is first, family is next, and pursuing His calling with excellence falls third. And I named it exactly what God whispered to me: She Works His Way.

(Can you see now why my husband jokes I've either birthed a business or a baby every year since 2010? It's

slightly exaggerated…but not by much!)

Our community is growing daily. I've got a team working with me who blow me away with their abilities. I can't believe the talent God has put together, and I'm so grateful to serve alongside these incredible women. And we're not done yet.

Closing Thoughts

I PROMISED I WOULD WRAP THIS UP, so let me close it this way. If you remember nothing else from reading this book, remember this:

Amazing things happen when we boast in our weaknesses.

2 Corinthians 12:9 reminds us, "My grace is sufficient for you, for My power is made perfect in weakness." Therefore, I will boast all the more gladly about my weaknesses, so that Christ's power may rest on me."

That's my life's theme verse.

As you know from my story, I did fitness completely wrong. But God developed me into a fitness professional.

I am fashion-challenged. I can't keep up with what's trending even if I try, but God called me to start a clothing line. It stretches me out of my comfort zone to my core, but there's evidence He is using it, so I'll remain as comfortably uncomfortable as long as He calls me to serve Him here.

And She Works His Way? I'm not perfect. I don't get it right every time. But I'm not leading these women years after I've "been there, done that." I'm in the trenches with them.

I'll confess to you: it's hard. There are many days when it would be much easier and more selfishly beneficial to work my way.

But I've seen where disobedience led me.

I may never forget being that girl, just lying on that path, just waiting to die…but I also never have to be her again. Because just as I know where disobedience leads, I also know that choosing to obey God has never let me down.

So I'm not perfect, but I am willing to fight for obedience. To fight for living His way instead of my own.

For that, in the words of the apostle Paul, "I will fight the good fight. I will finish the race. I will keep the faith" (2 Timothy 4:7).

I may not know you or your struggle, but I do know that our God is bigger than whatever you're facing. My way let me down, and yours will too. But His way never fails.

Release the addiction of control, and embrace a life of sweet surrender to Jesus. That's my prayer for myself, and it's my prayer for you as well.

APPENDIX A:
WHEN A DIET
BECOMES A DISEASE

———————◆———————

MOST PEOPLE, ESPECIALLY WOMEN, HAVE BEEN ON A diet at some point in their lives. There is nothing wrong with making efforts to eat healthier or wanting to lose a few pounds. However, here are some symptoms that should pose as warning signs to you that a diet has crossed over to become a disease.

1. **When weight drops below 85-90% of the normal weight recommended for your height.** (Also, children and teens should be gaining weight as they grow and mature. Even if you don't notice rapid weight loss during adolescence, lack of weight gain could be a warning sign as well.)

2. **Intense fear of gaining weight or becoming fat.** (Pay attention to how they behave around people with weight problems. Most people will not come out and admit a fear of being fat, but you can learn a lot by seeing how they treat people who are overweight.)

3. **Constantly thinking about food.** (Calorie counting, spending abnormal amounts of time reading books and magazines about nutrition, planning all meals in advance, refusing to eat anything without knowing exactly what is in it, spending so much time talking and thinking about food, but never branching out and eating anything out of their set routine.)

4. **Menstrual cycle disappears.** (Body fat is not high enough for their body to ovulate. If a woman couples anorexic behavior with obsessive exercise, loss of menstrual cycle may occur before reaching a dangerous weight due to their high activity level.)

5. **Distorted perception of body image.** (Complaining about certain body parts or the way their clothes fit, comparing themselves to others, insisting that they need to lose weight, etc.)[19]

APPENDIX B:
FOR FAMILY & FRIENDS
OF AN ANOREXIC

———————◆———————

A NOREXIA CAN BE ONE OF THE MOST CONFUSING disorders for someone to understand if they've never experienced it for themselves. This book has given you a peek into the mind of someone who has personally battled an eating disorder but I've specifically written this section for you: the parent, the sibling, the friend, etc., who is struggling with how to handle the anorexic victim in your life.

Before I go into some steps, the first thing to note is that each individual will be different. Some things you can say and do will help some anorexics, while the very same actions will harm others. The best advice to follow is Proverbs 16:9, *"A man's heart plans his way, but the Lord directs his steps."*

Always follow the prompting of the Holy Spirit. Be sensitive to His voice, and follow in obedience to what He says. His counsel is far greater than any advice I could ever give you. However, here are some guidelines that I've found to be generally true for myself and other girls I know who have battled similar struggles.

I would also like to note that I do realize that eating disorders are not exclusive to females. I know that guys battle them as well but because I can only speak for myself and the women I have counseled, these guidelines will be geared more towards helping female victims

Preventing the Problem

Model Healthy Behavior

The best thing you can do to prevent eating disorders among your loved ones is to model healthy behavior. Say no to crash diets, multiple trips to the gym per day and criticizing what you see when you look in the mirror. Health is more important than any habit you may have developed over the years.

You may have unhealthy habits that you don't even realize could be harmful to those who look up to you. For example, while I was growing up I remember my mom getting up several times every meal to serve someone in my family. By the time we were finished eating, she had only eaten a few bites.

Did she eat later? Of course. But she didn't eat with us. Though my mom's motivation of serving our family came from a good place, I remember using her behavior as justification for only nibbling at my food.

According to the Food Marketing Institute, less than half of American families eat dinner together. Even among these families, it only happens two or three nights a week. Be intentional about making sure that your family eats together most nights of the week and that you are setting a good example of balance and moderation for those you influence.

Be overly careful with the words you use.

Just last week, I was at the grocery store, and I saw a little girl ask her mom if they could buy a box of cookies. Her mother gasped. "No!" she exclaimed. "We don't eat cookies.

Cookies make you fat. You don't want to be fat, do you?" The little girl shook her head and dropped the cookies like they were on fire. The mother walked away with a look of satisfaction. I was horrified.

I wish I could tell you that was a one-time experience but unfortunately it's now normal for young girls to make enemies with food before they are out of elementary school. Never allow yourself to believe the lie that someone is too young, too strong or too confident for your words to make a negative impact.

People with food allergies or restrictive diets may be more susceptible to developing an eating disorder later in life.

I don't have any research to back this up, but from what I've seen, kids that are either abnormally picky or grow up with food restrictions seem to be more prone to developing an eating disorder. Why? Because eating has never been normal for them.

Whether someone is diabetic, lactose intolerant or has a gluten allergy, they have grown up with foods that were "off limits." They have never been able to eat whatever they want. So whether it's because they are able to use their allergy or disorder as an excuse or because they are used to denying themselves of foods they wish to enjoy, they may be at a higher risk of developing an eating disorder.

<u>**When It's Already A Problem...**</u>

Tell her she is beautiful....but don't let your affirmation end there.

Most people get the first half of this one. I doubt you would be able to find a book pertaining to females that would say, "A woman doesn't need to be affirmed in her appearance. Don't waste your breath telling her how beautiful she is." Telling a woman she is beautiful is not new information.

I love the analogy John and Stasi Eldridge wrote in *Captivating: Unveiling the Mystery of a Woman's Soul*, "As little girls, we begin twirling for our daddies in our pretty dresses, asking, "Daddy, am I beautiful?" As we age, our dresses may have less bows and frills, but the question remains the same."

Obviously, women struggling with an eating disorder desperately long to know that they are beautiful. They may not believe you when you say it and may not even acknowledge your compliment. In fact, while I was anorexic, I probably heard the words, "You are so beautiful," more than any other time in my life. But even though I never believed the words, I still heard them. Those were not wasted words.

During my struggle, Satan was constantly whispering in my ear, "You're not pretty enough. You're not skinny enough. You're not worth anything." Any words that can combat those thoughts, even if they don't appear to be internalized, are needed. Even if you feel like she rejects you every time you compliment her appearance, never stop saying it. You never know when God may use that phrase to break her of the path of destruction she is on.

However, it's not that simple. So many people in my life were worried about my body image that they validated my beauty almost every time they saw me....to the point that I was convinced that my appearance was the only thing that mattered. Being beautiful was more than my goal. It was more than my obsession. It became my identity.

If I wasn't beautiful, who was I?

If I wasn't beautiful, what else could I do to get approval?

If I didn't stay thin, would I lose favor with everyone in my life?

So when you tell a woman she is beautiful, don't forget to also mention the other wonderful things she brings to your life. Does she make you laugh? Is she smart? Is she great with children? Can she instantly make strangers feel like friends?

Every person has unique gifts and abilities. Some talents are really easy to spot, such as an incredible singing voice or someone with a 4.0 GPA. Other abilities, though, like being a fantastic hostess, a good listener, a natural-born administrator, or even just a trustworthy friend, are not often referred to as "talents." But that's exactly what they are.

So, again, make sure she knows you think she is beautiful, but make sure she also knows that beautiful is not the only thing she is. She has much more to offer the world than a pretty face and a skinny silhouette.

Listen more than you speak.

Many times, I wished someone would have listened to what I was really saying instead of just hearing the words that were coming out of my mouth. I may have been verbally saying, "I'm just tired," but what I really meant was, "I'm so tired of living this way. Please make it stop."

Ask a lot of questions. Wait for opportunities where they may be more likely to open up. Pay attention to body language.

As I mentioned earlier, the eating disorder is what it is, but individuals are still people - not disorders. No matter what was said to me, I doubt I would have listened. I think it's why God had to use drastic measures to help me realize the severity of my problem.

Never give up.

Years after my recovery as I sit here and type this, I'm still in tears when I think about the unselfish love and support my family and friends continue to extend to me. I can't imagine how much I frustrated them.

I lied to them. I ignored them. I lashed out. I pulled away. I became a mere shell of the person I used to be. There was very little of a relationship with me that could have been edifying or encouraging.

Yet, they believed in me, they never gave up and they never stopped praying. They never stopped caring. No matter how many times I pushed them away, they always came back.

If you find yourself dealing with someone who is a professed Christian dealing with similar struggles, I encourage you to memorize Philippians 1:6, "For I am confident of this very thing, that He who began a good work in you will perfect it until the day of Christ Jesus."

APPENDIX C: RECOMMENDED RESOURCES

Bible Doctrine, Wayne Grudem. Grand Rapids: Zondervan, 1999.

Breaking Free: Discover the Victory of Total Surrender, Beth Moore. Nashville: Broadman and Holman Publishing, 2000.

The Incredible Power of Kingdom Authority: Getting an Upper Hand on the Underworld, Adrian Rogers. Nashville: Broadman and Holman Publishers, 2002.

Intuitive Eating: A Revolutionary Program that Works, Evelyn Tribole and Elyse Resch. New York: St. Martin's Press, 2003.

Lies Women Believe: And the Truth that Sets Them Free, Nancy Leigh Demoss. Chicago: Moody Publishers, 2001.

Mere Christianity, C.S. Lewis. San Francisco: HarperSanFancisco, 2001.

Plan B: What Do You Do When God Doesn't Show Up the Way You Thought He Would?, Pete Wilson. Nashville: Thomas Nelson, 2009.

When Godly People Do Ungodly Things: Finding Authentic Restoration in the Age of Seduction, Beth Moore. Nashville: Broadman and Holman Publishers, 2002.

———◆———

Myers Cross Training: myerscrosstraining.com

Cross Training Couture: crosstrainingcouture.com

She Works His Way: sheworksHisway.com

APPENDIX D: REFERENCES

1. http://www.anred.com/stats.html
2. Shari Graydon, *In Your Face: The Culture of Beauty and You* (Toronto: Annick Press, 2004)
3. B. Caballero and S. Rubinstein, "*Is Miss America an Undernourished Role Model?*," The Journal of the American Medical Association 283, no. 12 (March 2000): 23.
4. David G. Myers, *The Inflated Self: Human Illusions and the Biblical Call to Hope* (New York: Seabury, 1980).
5. www.barna.org
6. Revelation 12:9
7. Genesis 3:5
8. Genesis 3:3
9. John 10:27
10. Matthew 4:10
11. John 8:44
12. Matthew 4:11
13. James 4:8
14. Hewitt, P.L., & Flett, G.L. (1991). "*Perfectionism in the self and social contexts: Conceptualization, assessment and association with psychopathology.*" Journal of Personality and Social Psychology, 60. 456-470.

15. 2 Corinthians 9:6-11; Job 4:8; Psalm 126:5; Proverbs 22:8; Jeremiah 12:13; Hosea 10:12; Matthew 6:26; John 4:36-37; Galatians 6:7-8
16. Exodus 14
17. II Kings 2
18. Daniel 6
19. *Diagnostic and Statistical Manual of Mental Disorders* (DSMIV) 4th ed. (Washington, D.C.: American Psychiatric Association, 1994)

Made in the USA
Columbia, SC
20 November 2020

25035237R00114